Fascination and Terror

Documentation Centre Party Rally Grounds
The Exhibition

Content

4 Prefaces
6 The Congress Hall
14 Documentation Centre Party Rally Grounds
27 The Exhibition
112 Appendix
113 Organisation Chart

3

Dr. Ulrich Maly
Lord Mayor of the
City of Nuremberg

Nuremberg's Culture of Remembrance

Up until today Nuremberg, as few other German cities, has seen itself confronted with the historical legacy of the National Socialist era. Declared "City of the Party Rallies" in 1933, the Race Laws were passed here during the 1935 Party Rally, enshrining in law the outlawing of the Jews and other minorities, thus paving the way for the Holocaust. Nuremberg also lent its name to the trials which took place after the war to try and sentence the worst war criminals. In contrast to numerous memorials which commemorate victims of NS terror in former concentration camps or Gestapo prisons, the former Party Rally Grounds are a historical site recalling the enthusiastic spectators, hangers-on and in the widest sense, the perpetrators of NS policies. One cannot treat these stone remains entirely pragmatically. They must be associated with a historical judgement and a definite statement of our democratic community.

In 2001, the Documentation Centre was opened, as a contemporary exhibition centre which is open all year. With financial support from the Federal Government, the Free State of Bavaria and the district of Middle Franconia, as well as from foundations and private donors, the Centre's conceptual aspects are supported by an extremely dedicated committee. Each year, for over 200,000 visitors from all over the world, the Documentation Centre now provides definitive answers to the questions about the history of this place. And here, where once masses of people were considered little more than stage-managed puppets of the powers that be, the emphasis is now on the permanent responsibility of the individual for the safeguarding of human rights. In 2000, this project was accepted as the official German contribution to the UNESCO "International Year for a Culture of Peace".

We must never stop remembering. The City of Nuremberg is conscious of its particular responsibility in dealing with this stone legacy of the NS era. The former Party Rally Grounds are a national legacy. We will continue to address this historical period. At this site, a site of the perpetrators, we can thus also commemorate the millions of innocent victims and their families. And keep alive the exhortation "Never again!"

Learning from history

Friedrich Nietzsche warned against "revering history more than life". He saw "historical illusion" as a danger for life. Contemporary research on German history of the first half of the 20th century had to deal with exactly those problems exposed by Nietzsche. But even if a long phase of uncertain reflection and hesitant attempts towards realisation preceded the Documentation Centre Party Rally Grounds, one can now see in all clarity in this exhibition what happened here between 1927 and 1938: the NSDAP Party Rallies, stage-managed displays of political power, blasphemous, pseudo-religious cult worship events, celebrated very much in the style of a secularised pontifical mass, with maximum impact on the national, psychological and emotional mood.

In Nuremberg, as elsewhere, the fascination with violence ended in the inferno of total war: in the end, the "City of the Party Rallies" lay in ruins, burned out, and bombed. Between 20 November 1945 and 16 October 1946, there followed the International Military Tribunal with indictment, judgement and execution of the sentences. With Hitler's thugs sitting in the dock of the historical courtroom, the Nuremberg Trials were the beginning of a new legal concept, which the UN ratified in 1950 in the form of the "Nuremberg Principles."

Now we have continued this process which started with the Documentation Centre and established a "Memorial Nuremberg Trials", commemorating the military tribunal against Hermann Göring and his fellow defendants. The concerted, international attempt to find universal consensus on the necessity and legitimacy of the trials was not only about historical documentation, it was about much more: it was concerned with demonstrating to the entire world and for all time that the Nuremberg Trials of the main war criminals were necessary and legitimate. But they will only have a lasting historic effect if today and in the future, everything is done to expose clearly the legal, ethical, religious and moral reasons which formed the basis of these trials, and if we act according to those principles. By drawing the correct lessons from history, we honour the victims of violence.

Dr. Oscar Schneider
Spokesperson of the
Committee for the
Documentation Centre
Party Rally Grounds

The Congress Hall

Via stair wells and galleries, the U-shaped ring structure was to give access to the congress hall, accommodating 50,000 spectators in the stalls and various circles. The wings were to contain various function rooms.

Model view of the front of the Congress Hall, postcard from the 1930s.

On 11 September, 1935, Adolf Hitler, witnessed by 6,000 spectators, laid the foundation stone for the new Congress Hall on the shores of Dutzendteich lake. The pompously staged ceremony marked the beginning of the "Party Rally of Freedom", in the course of which the ignominious "Nuremberg Laws" were to be proclaimed. The monumental building, once referred to by Hitler as a "colossus", was to provide space for 50,000 people during congresses held in the course of the one-week party rallies. The Congress Hall was never completed. When building ceased in 1939, the hall had only reached about 60 per cent of its projected height. Nevertheless, this gigantic unfinished building with its base of 275 x 265 metres (inner court yard 180 x 160 metres), is the largest remaining relic of the architecture of power of the "Third Reich" in Germany. The plans were originally initiated by the City of Nuremberg who had commissioned the architect, Ludwig Ruff, with designing a Congress Hall, even before Albert Speer had taken on the overall planning task for the Party Rally Grounds. When Ruff died, in 1934, his son Franz took over the project.

In order to underline the show character of planned party congresses, Ruff – always in close consultation with Hitler – based his floor plan on examples from theatre architecture. The U-shaped main building was to comprise a central hall, finished off towards Dutzendteich lake with two wings and a connecting section. A pillared hall – which was also never built – topped with a gigantic four-horsed chariot, was to be erected in front of the connecting section. The entire round of the Congress Hall was to be surrounded by a flight of steps joining up with the arcades. The façade design is reminiscent of the Coliseum in Rome, but here, the language of power architecture is much more prominent. The smooth granite facing, the row of blind windows (glassed today), the plain arcade arches, all these elements were intended to signalise both the undisguised claim to power of National Socialism and its demand for unconditional subordination.

Top
View of the interior model, postcard from the 1930s.

Bottom
Hitler discussing the designs for the Congress Hall, on the occasion of a visit to the studio of architect Ruff, 1937.

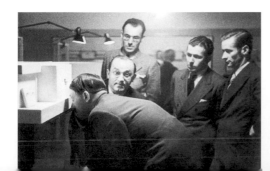

From top to bottom

Preparations for the laying of the foundation stone, September 1935.

The building site of the Congress Hall, decorated for the solemn laying of the foundation stone, September 1935.

Rammers during the difficult process of laying the foundation in swampy ground, 1936.

Before building could start, incredibly elaborate preparations had to take place, permanently transforming the traditional leisure and recreation area around the large Dutzendteich lake. Popular leisure facilities, such as the public baths in Bayernstraße, and the distinctive lighthouse, built on a corner of the lake for the 1906 State Exhibition, were demolished. Parts of the zoo which was adjacent in the west, also had to make way for the building site: some glass houses, animal houses and food stores were taken down. By 1939, the entire zoo had been transferred to Schmausenbuck, further east. Last, but not least, 850 trees had to be felled, and because of time pressure, their roots were not dug up with picks and axes, but blown up with explosives.

Then, the ground was levelled off, and a gigantic building site was established. For transport of building materials, a five track railway shunting yard was constructed near Luitpold Grove, and from here, materials were transported to the various building sites. Laying the foundation for this monumental Congress Hall proved to be complicated. First of all, a bulkhead had to be erected, shoring off the building site against Dutzendteich lake.

Top
Bricklayers working on the
Congress Hall, about 1938.

Bottom
Advertisement for the
"Arbeitsgemeinschaft
Kongresshalle Nürnberg"
(Association Congress Hall
Nuremberg).

The iron shuttering had to be rammed into the ground to a depth of six metres, using steam-powered rammers. After extensive and very difficult soil testing, the direction of works of the municipal building department decided to pack the soil, which was suffused by several groundwater streams, using about 22,000 acid-proof supports of roughly 10 metres length fashioned from quartz sand and granite chips. On top of this, a concrete foundation of over three metres' thickness was cast for the Congress Hall. Three major building firms, Siemens-Bauunion (Berlin), Philipp Holzmann (Munich) and Hochtief AG (Munich) formed the "Association Congress Hall" and were commissioned with the building of the shell. The price for the building quoted by them was 42 million Reichsmarks. Because of time pressure – the building was supposed to be finished by 1943 – a realistic estimation of costs was never presented. A 1935 calculation had estimated the building costs at 60–70 million Reichsmarks. But costs kept exploding, and in the end even the erection of the shell of the building considerably exceeded this sum.

The round building was erected between summer 1937 and the beginning of World War II, on 1 September, 1939. It consisted of six ring walls constructed from bricks and harder clinker bricks right up to the bordering moulding of the second floor, at a height of 39 metres. Had the building been completed, it would have been almost 80 metres high. The two wings were built to an intermediate height of about 16 metres. During this building phase, about 1,400 people worked on the building site, in double shifts of eight hours which were sometimes increased to ten hours. Work on Sundays and overtime was taken for granted. All commissioned companies were obliged to use helpers from other German regions so that less well-off regions could also participate in the building boom created by this major building project. 135 brickworks fulfilled the massive demand for conventional building materials, and according to the building materials office, until 1939 they supplied 42 million bricks.

Hitler (wearing a cape) during a
site visit, to the left the full scale
model of a façade segment.

In order to test the visual effect of this monumental building, the
direction of works had full scale models of various elements prepared.
In 1937, a wooden model of a segment of the Congress Hall façade was
erected south of the building site on the shore of Dutzendteich lake and
remained there until the war. At the summit of the Congress Halls curve,
a model of the interior, some 50 metres wide and 25 metres high, was
erected on the first floor; it comprised eight pillars, and was finished,
painted and suitably lit. A few months after its completion in February
1939, this segment was taken down again so as
not to obstruct further building.

On the outside, the brickwork of the
Congress Hall which was several metres
thick, was faced with granite. The
granite stones were 80
to 90 centimetres thick
and came from over
80 quarries in almost all German granite regions. This was high quality
natural stone, personally selected by Hitler for its colour and graining,
from stone lists prepared by the Ruff studio. All representation rooms
open to the public were also to be faced or decorated with marble or granite. Two halls in the north wing give an impression of what these rooms
might have looked like. In 1939, in one of the planned reception halls,
twelve Rotscheck limestone pillars from Adnet near Salzburg ("Adnet
Marble") were put up, and the adjacent anteroom contains two smaller
pillars fashioned from Löbejün porphyry. The interior decoration was
never completed. Both halls are now part of the Documentation Centre.

The roof above the huge main hall was to be a cantilever steel
construction. In July 1939, twelve companies established the "Steel
Construction Association Congress Hall Nuremberg" (ASKO), to take on
this construction job. In early 1940, they all agreed to cease planning,
since building work had more or less been discontinued. After the war
had started, because of conscription, the number of building workers

From top to bottom

Night shift on the Congress Hall building site, 1936.

The interior model at the summit of the Congress Hall curve, 1939.

In 1944, a light anti-aircraft gun was installed on top of the building in order to protect the Congress Hall from air raids. It was manned with young flak helpers.

had decreased from the original number of 1,400 to 40 in December 1939. The staff of the direction of works had also been reduced, and in the following years fluctuated between 20 and 200 persons. Some masonry work and sporadic planning activities were continued up until 1943, with prisoners of war used for laying bricks, too.

Several air raids on Nuremberg during the war resulted in considerable damage to both the main body and the wings of the Congress Hall. In 1943/44, the direction of works ordered some safety measures: all openings to the outside were bricked up and weight-bearing partition walls were erected inside the building. Some of the rooms thus created were used for storing army supplies. Most of the space was, however, used by the Maschinenfabrik Augsburg-Nürnberg (MAN) for manufacture, with up to 900 people employed there. Additional offices and an operating theatre with two rooms for beds were established on the ground floor, as an alternative ward for the auxiliary hospital "Alter Tiergarten".

Left
German Building Exhibition
of 1949 in and in front of the
"Round Exhibition Building",
the name given to the unfinished
shell, in order to avoid the
ideologically tarnished name
"Congress Hall":

Right
Café Königshof on the second
floor, during the 1949 German
Building Exhibition.

After 1945, the Congress Hall became the property of the City of Nuremberg. In the post-war years, the unfinished monumental building was referred to as the "Round Exhibition Building", because the name "Congress Hall" was not considered politically correct. In September 1949, the hall and the adjacent outdoor area were the venue for the "German Building Exhibition" (Deutsche Bauausstellung DBA) which had been instigated by the "Committee for the Reconstruction of Nuremberg", with the intention of "contributing to the rehabilitation of the reputation of the City of Nuremberg which has suffered considerably all over the world because of the political events of the past years". 500 companies from both at home and abroad participated in the exhibition which attracted 300,000 visitors. Nine months later, from 14 to 30 July, 1950, the City of Nuremberg celebrated its 900th anniversary. As in the previous year, the second, unfinished, floor served as a restaurant with a panorama terrace overlooking the inner courtyard. In subsequent years, the Congress Hall was the venue for various events, such as shows of traditional dress or reunions of exiles. Soon, however, the provisional character of the round building

Trivial use during several decades, up until 2001, also comprised storage of building materials, mobile toilet containers and impounded cars on the inner courtyard of the Congress Hall.

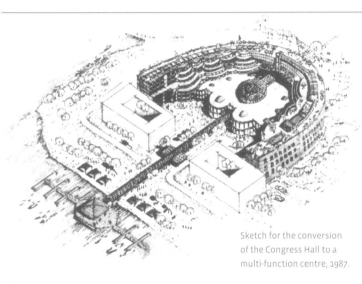

Sketch for the conversion of the Congress Hall to a multi-function centre, 1987.

no longer met the increased demands made of an exhibition and trade fair hall. Suggestions for the future included use as an exhibition hall, a camp for mass meetings, a football stadium, a drive-in cinema, or an old people's home, as well as plans for blowing the building up. They all came to nothing, because people tended to underestimate the gigantic size and the resulting costs. In 1969, the City Council decided to use the complex in a very pragmatic way in the future: as a storage space, with a number of rooms rented out to various companies.

Ambitious commercial plans prepared by both the municipal administration and non-municipal financing bodies included the spectacular project suggested by a private company in 1987: the 500 million Marks conversion of the Congress Hall into a shopping centre. The Bavarian Office for the Protection of Historic Monuments rejected this plan, pointing out that the 1973 Law on the Protection of Monuments obliged the City of Nuremberg to maintain the structures, and that the project "was not suited to the special character of this historic monument". A citizens' initiative put forward the suggestion that the unfinished Congress Hall ought to be maintained as a historic monument, and they submitted a concept for this. Finally, the municipal administration withdrew its plans, after they had also been rejected by the City Council. In 1998, in the wake of the discussions concerning this project, the Culture Department held a symposium: "The Heritage: Dealing with Nazi Architecture". Up until then, this discussion had been almost exclusively dominated by pragmatic, financial and economic considerations – both in Nuremberg and elsewhere in the Federal Republic. There had been almost no references to the Nazi past. In the final discussion of this symposium, the then Deputy Mayor in Charge of Cultural Affairs, Hermann Glaser, suggested that Nazi buildings should be maintained and used "in a trivial way", accompanied by increased and intensified provision of information. The participants, among them renowned scientists and publicists, unanimously recommended that the building remains should be treated as "didactic material". Nobody was in favour of taking them down. The discussion about the plans for converting the Congress Hall into a leisure and shopping centre marked a turning point in the way Nuremberg dealt with the Nazi buildings on the former Party Rally Grounds.

Documentation Centre Party Rally Grounds

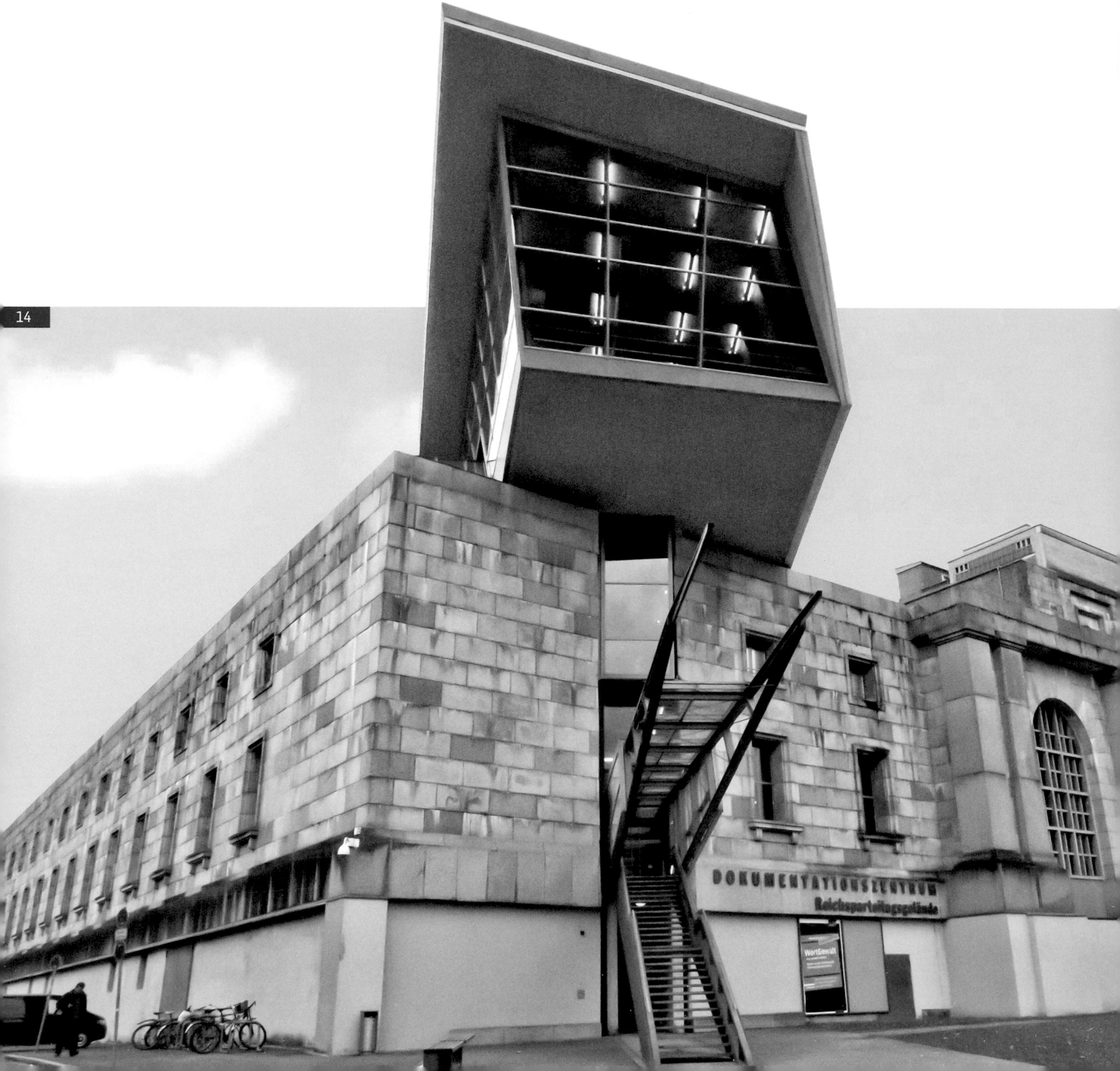

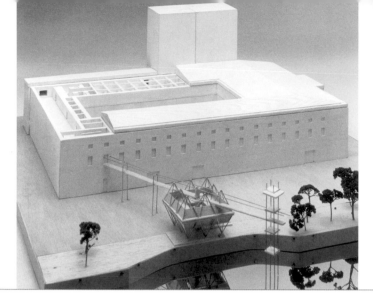

1985 was the key year for the development of a concept for dealing with the former Party Rally Grounds, with an increasing awareness of its history. During this year, heated discussions took place in the city, in the context of the plans for the 150th anniversary of the first German Railway – debating whether topics such as the role of the Reichsbahn in the deportation of Jews ought to be represented –, and in the Zeppelin Grandstand, the city's culture department opened an exhibition dealing with this historically incriminated area. Titled "Fascination and Terror", the exhibition provided information on the history of National Socialism, on Nuremberg's role as "City of the Party Rallies" and on the function of the National Socialist architecture of power. Since only 60.000 DM (30,000 Euro) were available for preparing this presentation, it was rather provisional in character, and because of insufficient heating facilities it could only be shown during the summer months. Slowly but surely, the insight prevailed that, in view of an increasing demand for information voiced by visitors from both at home and abroad, this provisional exhibition had to be replaced by a more permanent solution. The city government and representatives of all political parties considered that this task could only be taken on with support from both the Federal Republic and the Free State of Bavaria. Thus, in 1996, after visiting the grounds, the cultural committee of the German Association of Cities demanded that a public foundation be established to take on the grounds and look after the future development from a museum point of view. So far, this far-reaching demand has, however, not been met.

Nuremberg Municipal Museums took a much more concrete approach. The museums, after re-organisation in 1994, are also responsible for dealing with the historical aspects of the former Party Rally Grounds. In December 1994, the director of museums, Dr. Franz Sonnenberger, suggested that an all-year exhibition should be created in a new building which might also use parts of the northern wing of the Nazi Congress Hall. This project was part of a general overhaul of all municipal museums, to be completed for the city's 950th anniversary in 2000. The city's cultural committee unanimously adopted the concept proposed by the municipal museums. The city, however, declared that it was not able to provide the finances for this modernising programme. In the context of the "Year of Remembrance 1945–1995", which in Nuremberg was mainly characterised by the first presentation of the Nuremberg International Human Rights Award, a wide consensus was reached that something had to happen concerning the Party Rally Grounds. In this situation, the proposal put forward by Nuremberg Municipal Museums in 1996, of erecting an exhibition pavilion on the shore of Dutzendteich lake provided a modest, and very concrete architectural impulse, including the use of some rooms in the north wing of the Congress Hall. This design – however controversial from an aesthetic point of view – broke the ice. Representatives from politics, the media, the churches and other religious communities offered their support, and a 250.000 DM (125,000 Euro) donation made by the editor of the Nürnberger Nachrichten newspaper, Bruno Schnell, provided the financial basis for further plans.

Top left
Model of the first project for
the Documentation Centre,
which was to "set a sign" at the
Dutzendteich lake, 1996.

Right
Empty rooms in the northern
wing, 1997.

From left to right

Breaking the axis: virtual
horizontal projection of
Günther Domenig's design,
2000

Model of the winning design
by Professor Günther Domenig,
1998.

Virtual horizontal projection
of the Domenig building
programme: the Study Forum
on top of the north wing, the
stake piercing the building
diagonally and the suspended
cinema and lecture hall,
2000.

With wide support beyond all party political boundaries, two bodies were established which accompanied and passionately supported the project up until its completion in 2001. The committee set up by the then Lord Mayor, Ludwig Scholz, which elected former Federal Minister of Building, Dr. Oscar Schneider as its spokesperson, successfully campaigned for the project to be financed with contributions from the Federal Republic, the Free State of Bavaria, the City of Nuremberg, the Region of Middle Franconia and further public sponsors. In addition to this committee, a scientific advisory committee accompanied the project, supporting the concept, implementation and design for a new permanent exhibition "Fascination and Terror" which was entrusted to Nuremberg Municipal Museums. An expert report commissioned from the University of Erlangen-Nürnberg in 1997 on the future museum use of the Congress Hall was the starting point for the entire process.

In 1998, an architectural competition by invitation, for the planned Documentation Centre, was held by the City of Nuremberg, under the overall control of its Director of Building, Prof. Walter Anderle. The brief was not only to fit the Documentation Centre into the north wing of the Congress Hall so that it could function as a museum, but also to find a convincing way of dealing with the NS architecture and the spirit which had inspired it. Günther Domenig (1934–2012), professor of architecture from Graz, won the competition.

This was an unusual task for the architect, who in his private life constantly faces the challenge of dealing, in a critical way, with his own experiences as a young boy during the Nazi era: "The exhibition Documentation Centre Nuremberg Party Rally Grounds is a memorial in the truest sense of the word. The rudimentary building is an unbelievable demonstration of power with an external appearance which was intended for massed meetings staged in a monumental, militant way. The exhibition rooms of the Documentation Centre, both for the permanent show and for temporary exhibitions, immediately expose Fascist architecture.

One important and consistent element of this architecture is its axial nature. There is not one, not even the smallest, functional element in the rooms which does not demonstrate this intimidating ideology. So breaking this historic axis, and thus dealing with history, seems the obvious solution. I juxtaposed the existing symmetry and the ideology behind it with sloping, slanting lines. In order to counter the sheer weight of concrete, bricks and granite, I turned to lighter materials: glass, steel and aluminium. The historic walls remained unchanged and are nowhere touched by the new work." (Günther Domenig, Architektur und Bau Forum 3/2000)

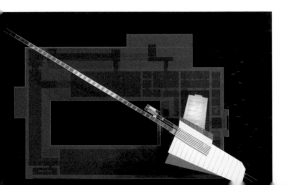

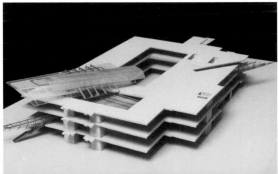

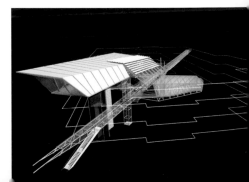

The foyer with stair
and suspended cinema
and lecture hall, 2001.

Domenig's intention is perfectly obvious at the north-eastern corner of the former Congress Hall. The granite façade was sliced open from top to bottom to provide an opening for the entrance. A slender steel stair and the support for the glass roof project from the narrow opening, at an angle. The stair leads through metres of unfinished brickwork to the first hall. This hall provides space for a reception area, offices, a glass lift shaft and the interior stair well, as well as a cinema and lecture room, clearly visible "interventions" with the existing building. For the cinema, new concrete girders had to be installed in the roof so that the hall could be suspended in the space above the foyer. The stair well gives access to the upper floor, and then via a bridge to the Documentation Centre's permanent exhibition. Domenig placed the Study Forum on top of the north wing, and it projects from the original building at an acute angle. Slanting steel frames define the two bright seminar rooms with their modern equipment, which also provide a panoramic view of the grounds across a large, suspended terrace.

It was an unusual building task, not only for the architect, but also for all others involved in the implementation of the design. During the planning phase, it became clear that existing building documents did not have reliable measurements, and the north wing had to be completely re-measured using modern methods. Any work requiring cuts through the existing building to enable a tour through the building had to be made with utmost precision. In addition to the facing consisting of granite blocks of 80–90 centimetres' thickness, the brick walls behind the facing, some of them up to one metre thick, had to be cut. This was achieved with rather unspectacular looking wire saws whose diamond wires cut easily through everything. The largest continual cut was eleven metres deep. Thinner walls and the concrete ceilings were cut with large circular saw blades.

The most noticeable element of the building for the Documentation Centre certainly is the glass "stake" piercing the massive walls and effectively disturbing the rectangular geometry of the NS building. A corridor of two metres' width and 130 metres' length cuts through the entire north wing and across its large, partly finished and still open-roofed representation halls. At the end of their tour of the exhibition, visitors arrive at the southern end of the stake which projects from the building into the inner courtyard at this point. Seen from this angle, the gigantic round building looks like a massive quarry for bricks. On the way back along the corridor, which leads back down to the foyer, visitors are given unusual insights into the building. So far, the architecture of the Documentation Centre has received several awards. In 2004, the City of Nuremberg honoured the building with the city's architectural award, and on the occasion of the Architectural Biennial in Venice in the same year, Günther Domenig was presented with the "Golden Palm" for this building.

From left to right

First cut is the deepest; opening the facade, 2000.

The upper end of the "stake", 2000.

View of the "stake" threaded through the large pillared hall.

View from the foyer
along the stake with its over
100 metres length, 2001.

From top to bottom

One of the later exhibition rooms in its original state, 1997.

Virtual view of the same room during the planning phase, 2000.

The real exhibition room, 2014.

One of the particular advantages of this design is its sensitivity to the didactics of the exhibition. Specific developments made possible an almost ideal round tour of the upper floor of the north wing. This provided about 1,300 square metres of exhibition space, all on one level (thus accessible for disabled visitors). The room sizes vary from 20 to 450 square metres. With very few exceptions necessitated by technical adaptations, such as bridging an air shaft between two stair wells or providing entrance facilities for disabled visitors, neither the architect nor the exhibition designers interfered with the substance of this protected building. Apart from a cast concrete floor which also contains the floor heating system, the exhibition rooms were left in their unfinished previous state as far as possible. On no account did the architect want to finish the task the National Socialist builders had not been able to complete. Rather the raw brickwork exposes the banality of megalomania, beyond all myths and glorifications. The exhibition design created by the studio Müller+Müller-Rieger also consistently kept a distance to the "exhibit Congress Hall". They structured the exhibition effectively with heavy steel plates used as partitions, and information panels consisting of room-high glass panes, which still look remarkably delicate compared to the clumsy and massive walls, thus sticking to the same materials Domenig had used for the external structure.

The focus of the newly designed permanent exhibition "Fascination and Terror" – keeping the title of the previous provisional exhibition in the Zeppelin Grandstand – is on the history of the Nazi Party Rallies.

The virtual entrance for the exhibition "Fascination and Terror", 2000.

Virtual representation of the Party Rally Grounds in a simulation of the exhibition room "Building History", 2000.

Virtual vision of the room about the building history of the rally grounds, 2000.

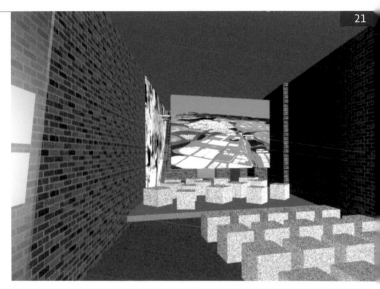

Since a lot of documents are available, the building history of the Party Rally Grounds is extensively presented. Following the input from the scientific advisory committee, the Nuremberg exhibition also points out the consequences of National Socialist mania and its millions of victims. This is why on the one hand it takes a "microscopic" look at the history of Nuremberg in order to highlight the local conditions necessary for the city's development to the "City of the Party Rallies". And on the other hand, via interspersed "historical windows", the exhibition presents a view of the essential elements making up a panorama of German and European history between 1933 and 1945. The exhibition is rounded off by information on the "Nuremberg Trials" and on the way the former Party Rally Grounds have been dealt with since the end of the war.

Right from the beginning, the question was not just one of content and form of the presentation, but also one of the intended target audiences. Very soon, there will be no more visitors who remember the Nazi era personally or through tales told by their parents or grandparents. With a younger visitor generation in mind, the exhibition makers had to find a type of presentation corresponding to the young people's understanding and receptive traditions. Thus Nuremberg Municipal Museums did not design an exhibition based mainly on exhibits, but rather a historic narrative illustrated by numerous pictorial, sound and film documents. Wherever this was considered meaningful, modern didactic methods of illustration are used, such as computer-generated reconstructions and electronic image storage media.

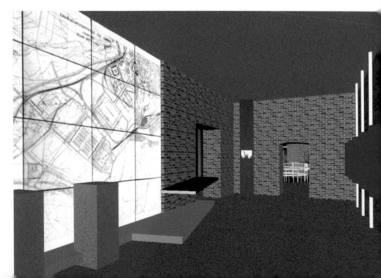

Top
A 660 square metre hall, which
served as a vehicle garage for
the THW (organisation providing
technical assistance in response
to disasters), is now used for
temporary exhibitions.

Bottom
Installation of the exhibit
"The Track. The Logistics of the
Racialmania", 2010

22

The audio guide system issued to every visitor also plays an outstanding role. Apart from providing the best access to the exhibition for non-German speakers, it also gives compact intro-ductions to each of the 19 exhibition topics as well as a glossary of important NS institutions. German-speaking visitors can also listen to all texts. This is a special provision for the younger generation which, as ex-perience has shown, is much less reading-oriented than the older generation. And not least the audio system was the precondition for the exhibition being under-standable without guided tours, which would hardly be possible in the exhibition rooms (some of them very small) without in conveniencing other visitors.

The costs for the building and for the preparation of the exhibition for the Documentation Centre were originally estimated as 18 million DM, with six million DM each to be paid by the Federal Republic, the Free State of Bavaria and the City of Nuremberg together with the Region of Middle Franconia. The final sum was 21.5 million DM, and the City of Nuremberg agreed to pay the extra sum and bear the running costs. Additional financial support for the project comes from foundations, public bodies and private sponsors, mainly from the city and region of Nuremberg. On 4 November, 2001, the then Federal President, Johannes Rau, opened the Documentation Centre Party Rally Grounds, in the presence of numerous high-ranking representatives from the state, from politics, and from general society, with major international media interest.

Aerial view of the Documentation
Centre Party Rally Grounds, 2001.
The photograph shows the dimensions of the overall building compared
to the institution housed in the
north wing (bottom of picture).

Camp Zone

Marchfield

Municipal Stadium

◄ Strength through Joy Town

German Stadium

Zeppelin Field

Great Road

Congress Hall

SS Barracks

Luitpold Arena

Aerial view over the former Nazi
Party Rally Grounds towards south.
The coloured parts are no longer
existent.

Satellite picture of Nuremberg
with the marked areas of the
medieval town and the former
Nazi Party Rally Grounds.

The Exhibition

1	Rise of the NSDAP in the Weimar Republic	28
2	The Seizure of Power	32
3	The Beginnings of the Dictatorship	34
4	"Führer" and "National Community"	38
5	The "Führer"-Myth	41
6	"City of the Party Rallies"	44
7	Building History of the Party Rally Grounds	48
8	Forced Labour for the NS-Construction Projects	56
9	The Party Rallies as Ritual	60
10	The Organization of the Nazi Party Rallies	66
11	The Event of the Nazi Party Rallies	70
12	The Response Abroad	78
13	"Triumph of the Will"	82
14	Racism and Anti-Semitism	86
15	The Way into War	92
16	The War of Annihilation and Genocide	94
17	The German Resistance	98
18	The Nuremberg Trials	101
19	The Nazi Party Rally Grounds after 1945	106

Rise of the NSDAP in the Weimar Republic

Germany after the First World War: The monarchy had been removed. In Weimar the country wrote a new constitution for itself. Yet the young republic was on shaky ground. Many Germans rejected the new democracy. To a large extent it became associated with the military defeat as well as with the humiliations of the Peace Treaty of Versailles that Germany had been forced to accept. The consequences of the war such as chaos, hunger, enormous public debts, and monetary depreciation at an ever accelerating rate were not blamed on the fallen Empire but rather on the Democratic parties. Until 1923 Germany was at the mercy of the dictatorship of the mob. Revolutions and uprisings from left and right were almost invariably followed by a state of emergency.

Leading politicians became the victims of assassins. Afterwards, too, acts of violence and the appearance on the streets of uniformed groups remained a part of everyday life.

It is only between 1924 and 1929 – in a phase of political and economic stability – that the republic seemed to prosper. But in 1929 the world economic crisis spread to Germany, too: Soon more than six million people were without work and adequate social provision. Spurred on by numerous election campaigns in rapid succession, a radicalization of political life took hold, which in 1933 finally crushed the republic.

Against this background followed the rise of the National Socialist Workers' Party and a man who left Austria in 1913 to come to Germany – Adolf Hitler.

The Beginnings of the NSDAP

The German Workers' Party, the forerunner of the National Socialist German Workers' Party (NSDAP), was founded in Munich in 1919. Thanks to his rhetorical talents Adolf Hitler, initially Werbeobmann (recruitment representative), then party chairman as of July 1921, transformed the sect-like group into an aggressive political party. The party was radically anti-Semitic, agitated against the Weimar Republic and its founders (the "November criminals"), against the Versailles "Treaty of Shame" and the "Policy of Compliance".

"German Day" 1923

Encouraged by the Bavarian government's anti-Reich and anti-republican stance, Bavaria became a gathering point for nationalistic, anti-democratic groups and associations of every shade. On September 2, 1923 the Vaterländische Verbände (Patriotic Fighters Associations) gathered in Nuremberg for "German Day". Hitler paraded his paramilitary SA (Storm Troopers) and stole the show from his rivals. He also forged a new confederation of armed defense leagues; SA, Bund Oberland (Oberland League) und Reichskriegsflagge (Reich War Flag) banded together into the Patriotic German Fighters League.

Left
NSDAP event in the Munich Bürgerbräukeller, 1923.
Right
"German Day" in Nuremberg: march-past of the SA on the Main Market Square, in front of Hitler and Julius Streicher, the publisher of the violently anti-Semitic propaganda rag "Der Stürmer" (The Storm Trooper), 2 September, 1923.

NSDAP followers on their way to the "German Day" in Coburg in October 1922. Second from the left: Adolf Hitler.

Die Angeklagten des Hitler-Prozesses.

Pernet Weber Frick Kriebel Ludendorff Hitler Brückner Wag
Röhm

The Hitler Putsch

In the fall of 1923 Hitler decided that the time was ripe to topple the Reich government. On November 9, in a "heroic" action, he marched into the Munich government district with armed supporters, primarily the "Patriotic German Fighters League". They were stopped by the Bavarian State police at the Feldherrnhalle. 15 rabble-rousers, four policemen, and an innocent by-stander were killed. The NSDAP was banned throughout the Reich. Later Hitler was to twist this fiasco into a triumph: those killed, heralded as "The Martyrs of the Movement", formed the basis for the NS Cult of the Dead.

The Hitler Trial

Charged with high treason, Hitler was not tried at the Reich Court in Leipzig, which actually had jurisdiction, but rather at the People's Court in Munich, where he could reckon with the political sympathy of the judge. It gave Hitler the opportunity to use the trial (26 February to 1 April, 1924) as a political platform and to create an image of himself as the true leader of the nationalist forces in Germany. He was given a very lenient sentence of five years' imprisonment in the old fortress of Landsberg. After half a year later he was released on probation by the Bavarian Supreme Court.

From left to right

Barricade with armed rebels in Munich, on 9 November, 1923; fourth from the left (with flag) is Heinrich Himmler.

The accused at the Hitler trial, Munich 1924.

Second NSDAP Party Rally: participants waiting for Hitler's arrival at the Goethe and Schiller monument, Weimar 1926.

Proklamation
an das deutsche Volk!

Die Regierung der November-
verbrecher in Berlin ift heute
für abgefetzt erklärt worden.

Eine provisorische deutsche
National-Regierung
ift gebildet worden.

Diese besteht aus

General Ludendorff, Adolf Hitler
General von Lossow, Oberst von Seisser

Proclamation by the rebels concerning the toppling of the government, 1923.

Title page of the NS Publication: "Hitler above Germany", published by Heinrich Hoffmann, Munich, 1932. Hitler was the first German politician to use planes in order to be able to address mass meetings in several cities on the same day.

A New Beginning and Reorganization

While in prison Hitler rethought his political strategy and re-examined his views and opinions, writing them down in *Mein Kampf*. To avoid another ban on the party, he now began to look for legal means of obtaining power, without giving up the street as a political forum. After the re-establishment of the party and the SA on 27 February, 1925, the new NS organisations of the Schutzstaffel (SS, elite defense units) and the Hitler-Jugend (HJ, Hitler Youth) were founded in 1925 and 1926, respectively. Hitler did not revise any of his political positions, however the struggle to "keep pure the Arian master race" and to acquire new Lebensraum (living space) in the East now took center ground in his thinking.

The Political Breakthrough

After refoundation of party and SA on 27 February, 1925 there was – from 1928 on – a gradual increase in the public's awareness of the NSDAP. The party stage-managed politics with theatrical aplomb. The party conducted election campaigns using men, materials and technology on a hitherto unknown scale. After achieving 18.3% of the votes in the Reichstag (German Parliament) elections of 1930, the political breakthrough was assured, and on 31 July, 1932 they became the strongest political party with a 37.4% share of the votes.

Headline of the Social Democratic magazine "Vorwärts" (Onward) of 5 August, 1929. According to police reports, 25,000 SA and SS men took part in the 1929 NSDAP Party Rally. Riotous fights with political opponents resulted in people being injured and killed.

The Seizure of Power

On the evening of 30 January, 1933 Hitler's supporters celebrated in Berlin. In a quickly organised torchlight parade SA and SS as well as members of the Stahlhelm, so-called Steel Helmets (a militant nationalist veterans' organisation), moved through the government district. Shortly before Reich President Paul von Hindenburg had appointed Adolf Hitler Reich Chancellor.

The National Socialists did not constitute the majority in the new government. Only three of the twelve cabinet members belonged to the NSDAP – they were Adolf Hitler, Wilhelm Frick and Hermann Göring. Hitler's National-Conservative partners wanted to "curb" and "tame" the leader of the NSDAP. Their goal was to use the mass basis of his party for their own purposes. With this strategy, however, they were simply paving the way forward for Hitler and the National-Socialists.

In the Reichstag, too, neither the NSDAP nor the governing parties taken altogether had a majority. Instead, like all cabinets since March 1930 the Hitler government took as its legitimisation the special rights the constitution gives the Reich President in times of emergency. With the help of these presidential cabinets, Hitler's predecessors had sought to establish an authoritarian government system. This explains why, when Hitler attained power, anti-democratic forces and ideas had already gained much ground.

Parade of the SA through the Brandenburg Gate, 1933

On the occasion of Hitler's appointment as Reich Chancellor, an improvised torch light parade of several thousand SA and SS members as well as members of the "Steel Helmet" took place in the centre of Berlin on the evening of 30 January, 1933. Since there were no photographs available which could be used for propaganda purposes, this march was re-enacted for the film "SA Man Hans Westmar" in summer 1933. This photograph shows the large film lights used for the scene. Onlookers are wearing light summer clothing.

The Hitler Cabinet of 30 January, 1933

Adolf Hitler: "Führer" of the NSDAP. From 1934 "Führer and Chancellor of the Reich". 1945 Suicide.

Wilhelm Frick: 1933 to 1943 Minister of the Interior, thus in a key position in the new cabinet; 1943 to 1945 Minister without portfolio and Reich Protector of Bohemia and Moravia. Sentenced in the "Nuremberg Trial" and executed in 1946.

Hermann Göring: NSDAP. First of all, Minister without portfolio, from May 1933, Reich Minister for Aviation. As Reich Commissioner for the Prussian Ministry of the Interior, and, from April 1933, as President of Prussia, he controlled the police force of the largest German state. From 1935 to 1945 he was Commander-in-Chief of the Air Force. He was indicted in the "Nuremberg Trial" of the main war criminals and sentenced to death. In 1946 he escaped execution by committing suicide.

Franz von Papen: Zentrum up until 1932. June to December 1932 Reich Chancellor. Vice-Chancellor until July 1934, in addition Reich Commissioner for Prussia from July 1932 to April 1933. From July 1934 to 1938, he was the diplomatic representative of the German Reich in Vienna, 1939–1944 in Ankara. He was indicted and acquitted during the "Nuremberg Trial".

Alfred Hugenberg: Leader of the DNVP. Owner of a large media concern which actively fought against the Weimar Republic. Reich Minister of Economy and Reich Minister for Agriculture and Alimentation. Resigned in June 1933 under pressure from Hitler.

Franz Seldte: industrialist, founder and leader of the Steel Helmet, a nationalistic veterans' association. Until 1945 Reich Labour Minister. He was indicted in one of the Nuremberg follow-up trials. He died in internment in 1947.

Standing, from left to right: Franz Seldte, Günther Gereke, Johann Ludwig Graf v. Schwerin-Krosigk, Wilhelm Frick, Werner v. Blomberg, Alfred Hugenberg. Sitting, from left to right: Hermann Göring, Adolf Hitler, Franz v. Papen.

The Beginnings of the Dictatorship

While large sections of the population shew approval or at least adopted a policy of wait-and-see, the NSDAP began to rapidly extend its power with a blend of legal or pseudo-legal measures as well as with overt violence. Democratic institutions such as the Reichstag or the governments of the individual states were eliminated – to some extent with their own support; unwanted public servants were removed from office.

In their fight against political opponents, the National Socialists did not hesitate at all to use state instruments of power. The first concentration camps were set up in March 1933.

Books were burnt, and above all the first boycotts against Jews took place, a premonition of the later extent of persecution and violence.

The other political parties and groups underestimated Hitler and the National Socialists. They were surprised at the speed and the brutality of the measures, shyed away from open confrontation or hoped that, through concessions to the new rulers, they might have retained remnants of their old influence. The plans of the coalition partners to curb Hitler failed miserably.

Headline of the "Berliner Morgenpost" stating that the Reichstag was set ablaze by a Dutch communist, 28 February, 1933.

The Emergency Decree for the Defense of Nation and State

On 27 February, 1933 the Reichstag was set on fire. The new government used the incident as an excuse for the mass arrests of political opponents. The Reichstagsbrandverordnung (Emergency Decree by the Reich President for the Defense of Nation and State) abolished fundamental rights and created a permanent state of emergency. Germany was on the way to becoming a dictatorship.

The Enabling Act

After Reich President Hindenburg had dissolved the Reichstag on 1 February, 1933 at the request of the government, new elections took place on March 5. With the use of state instruments of power, the government parties achieved a majority. On 23 March, 1933 they passed the Enabling Act (Law for Removing Distress from the People and the Reich) in the Reichstag with the support of the conservative bourgeoisie factions. From then on it was even possible for Hitler's cabinet to pass laws involving constitutional changes without Reichstag approval.

Early Concentration Camps

In the wake of the many arrests following the Reichstag fire the first concentration camps were set up. The inmates were subject to uncontrolled violence in the camps. It was mainly the SA and the SS who incarcerated their prisoners there.

The concentration camp Dachau was opened on 22 March, 1933. Under Theodor Eicke, its commandant since June 1933, it became the model for all regular concentration camps and the training center for concentration camp personnel. More than 30 000 of a total of 200 000 registered prisoners died until 1945.

Left
On 23 March, 1933, Hitler proclaims the Enabling Law in front of the Reichstag which met in the Berlin Kroll-Oper after the Reichstag burnt down.

Right
Prisoners arriving in Dachau concentration camp, 1933.

Right
SA men inciting
people to boycott
Jewish shops in Berlin,
1 April, 1933.

Bottom left
Book burning on
Erlangen castle square,
12 May, 1933.

Bottom right
Berlin Opera Square,
10 May, 1933.

The Boycott of Jewish Businesses

On April 1, 1933, the NSDAP organized a boycott of Jewish businesses throughout the Reich. The "Law for the Restoration of the Professional Civil Service" of 7 April, 1933, which made possible the dismissal of politically unpopular and "non-Aryan" civil servants, soon led to Jews also being removed from posts in public administration.

Book Burning

On 10 May, 1933 the German Students' Association, as part of a "Campaign against the Un-German Spirit", organized the burning of books at practically all of Germany's universities. Tossed on to bonfires were books of many authors. Some writers fled Germany. Others were gradually to discover that their works could not be published. As representatives for the works of many other writers, the following authors' books were burned: Karl Marx, Karl Kautsky, Heinrich Mann, Ernst Glaeser, Erich Kästner, Friedrich Wilhelm Foerster, Sigmund Freud, Emil Ludwig, Werner Hegemann, Theodor Wolff, Georg Bernhard, Erich Maria Remarque, Alfred Kerr, Kurt Tucholsky, Carl von Ossietzky.

"Führer" and "National Community"

"Führer" and "national community", the pillars of the state, formed the two basic myths of the Third Reich. Behind them was the creed, disguised by a pretence of science, that the Germans were a people through "a common bloodline" with a uniform "racial core", in other words a people whose essential character rested on identical genetic material.

The National Socialists perceived German history as the history of internal struggles and divisions, which during the Weimar Republic increasingly threatened the continued existence of the nation. National Socialism claimed to be able to end this process of what they alleged was "disintegration" and be able to bring about the "unity of the people".

In this sense the "Volksgemeinschaft", the "national community", was a radical program aimed at returning modern society, characterized by a multiplicity of values and interests, to a pre-modern state. The objective was to create a kind of tribal society in which one individual, thanks to special "gifts", could determine how his followers, who submitted to him unconditionally, should think and act.

"Coordination"

Within just one year the National Socialists destroyed all organizations and institutions embodying and supporting the pluralistic-democratic order. By June the NSDAP was the sole party. The federal structure of the Reich was dismantled. "Coordination" as it was termed extended to every kind of club and association. They were dissolved or unified into centrally controlled Reich "associations" or "leagues".

"Community" Instead of Society

The pluralistic and parliamentary order were replaced by a community established on a purely emotional level through elevating experiences and feelings. These created in the mind the sense of inward unity, of identification between the "Führer" and his people. The National Socialists thus preferred mass festivals in which the individual was reduced to an insignificant part of the whole and the whole was geared to the Führer.

Left
Celebration of a company group of the DAF (German Workers' Front) in the Nuremberg Zündapp works, before 1939.

Right
"Stew Sunday" as a community-building ritual, Berlin 1937.

Hitler Youth poster, 1930. All youth organisations were either integrated in the Hitler Youth or banned.

Panel with concentration camp badges for the various groups of inmates, as used in 1940/41.

Segregation Instead of Integration

As a union of people bonded together through a shared genetic heritage, the NS "Volksgemeinschaft" (national community) represented a community with a common destiny into which one could only be born. Hitler also regarded it as a meritocracy in the service of national and imperialistic goals. Only those who belonged to it could share in the promised national, economic, and social progress. Those who rejected it or fell short of the "racial", political, and moral norms were excluded from the community, were singled out or even physically "eradicated": political opponents, Jews, Sinti and Roma, Jehovah's Witnesses, homosexuals, so-called asocial elements, those with severe mental or physical handicaps.

Dachau concentration camp, 1930s.

Kennzeichen für Schutzhäftlinge in den konz. Lagern
Form und Farbe der Kennzeichen

	Politisch	Berufs-Verbrecher	Emigrant	Bibel-forscher	Homo-sexuell	Asozial
Grund-farben	▼	▼	▼	▼	▼	▼
Abzeichen für Rückfällige	▼	▼	▼	▼	▼	▼
Häftlinge der Straf-kompanie	▼⊙	▼⊙	▼⊙	▼⊙	▼⊙	▼⊙
Abzeichen für Juden	✡	✡	✡	✡	✡	✡
Besondere Abzeichen	△ Jüd. Rasse-schänder	▲ Rasse-schänderin	⊙ Flucht-verdächtigt	2307 Häftlings-Nummer		Beispiel
	P Pole	T Tscheche	▲ Wehrmacht Angehöriger	⬤ Häftling Ia		

The "Führer"- Myth

A cleverly constructed myth, behind which Hitler the man became less and less tangible, turned a social failure in real life into someone chosen by Providence to become the savior of his people and his nation. Hitler was deemed the greatest German, the greatest statesman, the foremost artist and master builder of the nation, after the outbreak of the war the greatest commander of all times. The myth described Hitler as a unique genius and yet at the same time he remained a simple man of the people, a man with no personal needs, "wearing himself out" in the service of his people.

Thus arose the illusion of a superman, equal to any task and infallible.

"I swear by God this scared oath: I will render unconditional obedience to Adolf Hitler, the Führer of the German nation and people, Supreme Commander of the Armed Forces, and will be ready as a brave solider to risk my life at my time for this oath."

Personal oath to Hitler sworn by German soldiers after 1934.

Absolute Authority of the "Führer"

After the death of Reich President Hindenburg on 2 August, 1934, Hitler took over that office as well. He then combined in his own person the three highest offices of state in the Third Reich: Reich President, Reich Chancellor and "Führer" of the State Party all in one with the title "Führer and Reich Chancellor". Hitler evaded all legal and institutional obligations. For what he did was to legitimize the fact that he stood above all others and exercised unlimited power – not with constitutional and legal norms, but rather with the myths surrounding him and the acclamation of the masses who believed in those myths.

Top
Hitler during the Thanksgiving Festival on Bückeberg near Hamlyin, October 1934.

Bottom
Hitler and SA Chief of Staff, Ernst Röhm, during the 1933 Party Rally. Fearing him as a potential rival, Hitler had the SA's leading men including Röhm and some other opponents within and outside the party murdered on 30 June, 1934, pretending that this was necessary to prevent a revolt planned by the SA ("Röhm-Putsch").

The "Führer" Cult

The cult surrounding Hitler was the form in which the Hitler myth expressed itself in German society and at the same time the motor which continually recharged it. Hitler consistently made the propaganda offices of Party and State the focus of the public's attention, comparable only to the cults surrounding Benito Mussolini and Josef Stalin. In this way the Hitler cult permeated the entire public as well as much of the private domain. In the long run, therefore, it was hardly possible for anyone to avoid the seductive powers of the Hitler myth.

The "Führer's" Photographer

The Munich press photographer Heinrich Hoffmann worked for the NSDAP from the outset. As Hitler's personal photographer he achieved a dominant position with his photo reports on Hitler. Hoffmann's photographs, published by the million in books and in the press, defined the official image of the "Führer" and thus promoted the Hitler myth.

Left
Members of the Hitler Youth as "guard of honour" next to a full size Hitler picture, Erlangen 1933.

Right
The party's intended "Führer" image was effectively spread with collectable pictures from cigarette packets.

Devotional objects: hand woven tapestry, brass bust, crystal bowl, 1930s.

"City of the Party Rallies"

The venue for the Party Rallies of 1927 and 1929 was chosen first and foremost for political and practical reasons: From early on the National Socialists had a strong base in Nuremberg and Middle Franconia; in addition, they were lent support by the chief of the state-run police.

Nuremberg's past as a Free Imperial City and as the city of the medieval Imperial Diets was easily adapted to the National Socialist concept of Empire or Reich. In Potsdam, the city that symbolized the Prussian state, Hitler, in a pompously theatrical spectacle in March 1933, had attempted to create the impression of standing in the tradition of Old Prussia. In Nuremberg the NS regime uses the slogan "From the City of the 'Reichstage' (Imperial Diets) to the City of the 'Reichsparteitage'" (Party Rallies). In this way the National Socialists claim to be completing German history. In the process, Nuremberg's industrial and working-class character is almost totally ignored.

The Early Party Rallies

Luitpold Grove with the monument for the fallen of World War I which had been completed in 1932, became a venue for the National Socialists' Party Rallies before 1933. After the ban on public speaking imposed on Hitler had been lifted, the NSDAP organised its third Party Rally from 19–21 August, 1927, for the first time in Nuremberg. The parade of the SA and SS was staged in Luitpold Grove. On the Main Market Square, "party soldiers" marched past Hitler. From 1–4 August, 1929, the fourth NSDAP Party Rally was held in Nuremberg. For the first time, the monument to the fallen erected in Luitpold Grove, but not yet officially opened, was integrated in the celebration honouring the dead. Hitler had all party members swear a personal oath to him, using the "blood flag". Numerous acts of violence against political opponents perpetrated by SA men overshadowed the event. Nuremberg City Council therefore refused permission for further NSDAP Party Rallies.

Nuremberg before 1933

The 19th century saw Nuremberg developing into the most important industrial city in Bavaria. Liberal policies and the workers' movement had strong backing from the population. Between 1920 and 1933 Social Democrats and Liberals governed the city under the highly respected Lord Mayor Hermann Luppe. They achieved considerable success in the areas of social welfare, housing projects, and city planning.

Hermann Luppe,
Lord Mayor of Nuremberg
from 1920–1933.

Top
In 1927, Hitler celebrated the first consecration of flags using the "blood flag" which became part of the ritual during all Party Rallies.

Right
Mass assembly on the Main Market Square during the 1929 Party Rally.

The NSDAP and Nuremberg

Owing to agitation by the "Franconian Führer" Julius Streicher and thanks to the support of the police chief Heinrich Gareis, the NSDAP was able to gain a foothold quite early on and do well at elections. This was one of the reasons why the Nazi Party Rallies took place in Nuremberg in 1927 and 1929. In March 1933 the NSDAP seized power in Nuremberg too and forced Lord Mayor Hermann Luppe to step down. His successor was the National Socialist Willy Liebel.

Julius Streicher,
Gauleiter of Franconia
and publisher of the
"Stürmer" (Strom Trooper).

Heinrich Gareis,
Nuremberg Chief
of Police from
1923–1933.

Willy Liebel, 1933,
Nazi Lord Mayor
from 1933–1945.

First march-past of the Bayreuth SA Storm Troop 8 with music, 1927.

Propaganda outing of the Upper Franconian SA to the Franconian Jura, 6 May, 1928.

The Stegmann Album

Wilhelm Stegmann (1899–1944) was an agricultural engineer and tenant farmer on a large estate. In 1926, he founded the NS party branch in Schillingsfürst and was a most popular speaker and agitator. In 1928, the constituency 26 Franconia returned the best election result in the entire German Reich, and within it, the region Rothenburg-Land – Stegmann's realm of power – took first place with 80% votes for the NSDAP. From 1930–1932 Stegmann commanded the SA Franken, drilling them to become an army for an insurrection to overturn the Weimar Republic. The about 300 photographs in the album date from this time. A selection was digitized for use in the exhibition and can be browsed virtually.

Around the turn of 1932/33 Stegmann fell out with Hitler and Gauleiter Julius Streicher and was dismissed from all offices and excluded from the party for "mutiny". He was arrested in 1936 and sentenced to 18 months in prison, then rented a state domain near Braunschweig. After being sent to the Eastern front in 1944, to "prove his worth", he was killed in action there.

The first Rothenburg SA in September 1928.

Joseph Goebbels addressing the Hitler Youth in Bayreuth, 1927.

Pictures on this page were taken from an album containing some 300 photos showing actions of SA-leader Stegmann in Franconia. The album has been digitalised for the permanent exhibition.

Adolf Hitler during the "Franconian Day" on Hesselberg, 1931.

SA "Führer" conference on the Schillingsfürst domain, 1931.

Stegmann Album

Appropriation of Tradition

National Socialism deliberately harked back to Nuremberg's medieval past as an important location for the Imperial Diets in order to present itself as a Protector and Renewer of the Reich. In 1933 Hitler raised the status of Nuremberg from that of the "City of the Reichstage" (Imperial Diets) to the "City of the Reichsparteitage" (Nazi Party Rallies). Lord Mayor Liebel named Nuremberg the "most German of all German cities". This appropriation of imperial tradition culminated in 1938 in the "Heimholung" (return home) of the imperial insignia and relics from Vienna to Nuremberg.

Top
Hitler in front of the insignia of German Emperors in St. Catherine's Church, 1938. They were brought from Vienna to Nuremberg after the "Anschluss" and were to remain there from now on.

Top right
The "Führer" plane circling above Nuremberg, 1934.

Right
Poster for an 1937 exhibition in the Germanisches Nationalmuseum.

Building History of the Party Rally Grounds

Monumental buildings erected for eternity – the principles of National Socialist state and party architecture were particularly visible in Nuremberg. Structures were to impress and intimidate, demand discipline and give a feeling of community. Architecture served propaganda and provided a demonstration of power.

As the self-appointed "Supreme Master Builder" Hitler involved himself in the major construction projects, often immersing himself in the detailed planning. His favorite architect from 1934 on was Albert Speer, chosen to execute his architectonic phantasies of power and domination. Speer was commissioned by Hitler not only to build the Party Rally Grounds. By 1950 he was to have converted Berlin into "Germania, Capital of the World".

Only very few elements for the Party Rally Grounds were ever completed, others did never get beyond the foundations or were only partly built as shells. Construction practically ceased at the beginning of World War II, while planning work continued until shortly before the end of the war.

Plans for the Nazi Party Rally Grounds

In 1934 the architect Albert Speer was commissioned to draft an overall plan for the Party Rally Grounds. The large expanse of ground was 11 km² in size. The Great Road formed the central axis. It was aligned to the imperial castle and the Old Town, thus providing a symbolic link between historical Nuremberg and what the Nazis dubbed the "Temple City of the Movement".

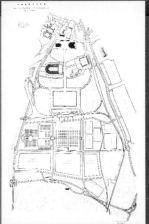

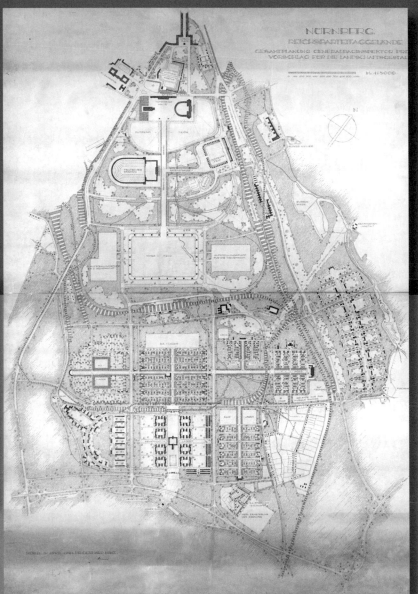

From left to right

Map of the Party Rally Grounds with Luitpold Arena, Congress Hall, Zeppelin Field and Municipal Stadium (from top), October 1934. The main grandstand of the Zeppelin Field is still shown on the eastern end here.

Map of the Party Rally Grounds, December 1937. For the first time, the SS barracks (top left) and the KdF Town (far right) are shown. The camp area is considerably larger. The largest building site which is clearly visible: the German Stadium left of the Great Street.

Coloured ideal map of the Party Rally Grounds for the Speer studio, prepared by garden designer Gerhard Hinz, commissioned with landscaping the Party Rally Grounds, April 1941.

The Luitpold Arena

A park next to the Luitpold Hall was converted into a marching field for 150,000 people. The altar-like structure was dominated by three gigantic flags and two bronze eagles on the side wings of the main stands. The Luitpold Arena was the venue for the Nazis' staged ceremonies honouring their dead, the "martyrs of the movement".

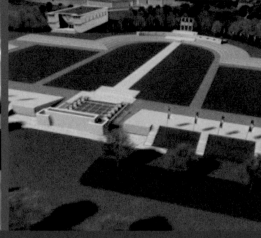

The Congress Hall

Hitler wanted a purpose-built structure seating at least 50,000 for the party congresses. The monumental Congress Hall was started on the shore of Dutzendteich lake, but was never completed.

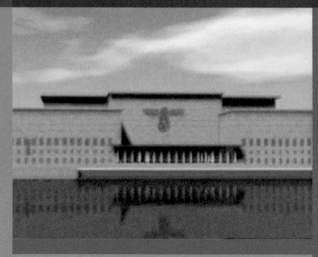

The Zeppelin Field

Speer designed the Zeppelin Field, which was converted between 1933 and 1937, as a fortress-like structure with ramparts and flag towers. The main grandstand was modelled on the antique Pergamon Altar. The Zeppelin Field is the only structure of party architecture which was completed.

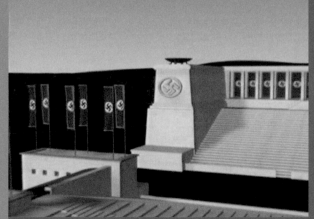
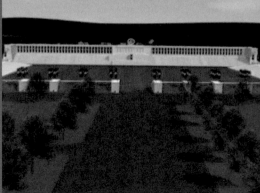

Pictures from a virtual simulation of the single Party Rally Grounds components shown in the permanent exhibition.

The Municipal Stadium

The municipal stadium built in 1928 lies next to the Zeppelin Field. For the Party Rallies, it was transformed with two wooden towers, widened entrance gates and the "Führer" rostrum. On the "Day of the Hitler Youth", between 50,000 and 60,000 young people had to parade here in front of the "Führer".

 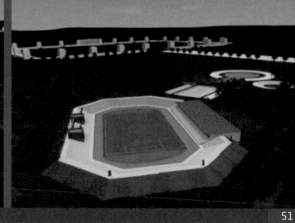

The Great Street

A parade street which is 60 metres wide and 2 kilometres long went from March Field to Luitpold Grove. In the north, it was aligned with Nuremberg's Imperial Castle. This was to create a symbolic link between the "City of the Imperial Diets" and the Party Rally Grounds.

The German Stadium

Over 400,000 spectators were to witness the NS Combat Games – a kind of German Olympic Games – in the German Stadium. The monstrous building was to be over 130 metres high, but never went beyond the excavation stage.

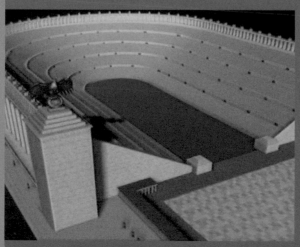 

March Field

The March Field, with its area of 700 x 900 metres, its ramparts and 24 defence towers was to act as a backdrop for the demonstrations of the Wehrmacht. These staged fight scenes were intended to prepare the Germans for war, both mentally and emotionally. The March Field was never completed.

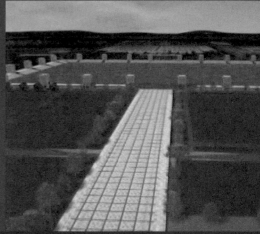

The Camp Areas

A lot of accommodation was needed for the enormous spectator numbers and for the various NS organisations involved in the massed parades, such as SA, SA, Hitler Youth, German Labour Service. South of the grounds, extensive tent and barrack camps were provided for this purpose.

The "Strength-Through-Joy" Town

In 1937, the KDF town (Strength through Joy town) was solemnly opened. Large beer halls, open-air theatres and bowling alleys were intended to increase the Party Rallies' entertainment value.

Message of architecture

"Never throughout all of German history have greater and nobler buildings been planned, begun, and completed than in our own time [...]. This is why these buildings are not intended for the year 1940, or for the year 2000, but, rather, they should reach out, like the cathedrals of our past, into the centuries of the future."
Hitler in Nuremberg, 7 September, 1937.

Backdrop

To create the appropriate setting for the concept of the Volksgemeinschaft Albert Speer surrounded the parade grounds of the Party Rally Grounds with massive grandstands and towers. The architecture, designed as an imposing backdrop was intended to lend the March Field and the Zeppelin Field a fortress-like atmosphere. The aim was also to give those assembled there as well as the public at large the impression that here was an integrated whole, a unified body ready to take up arms in its own defence.

Dimensions

The Nazi Party Rally Grounds – as a total entity and as individual buildings – were there to demonstrate National Socialist power to the world without and to those within. With their gigantic dimensions, the grounds and the architecture were meant to suggest to the individual visitor to the Party Rallies that he was participating in something major and significant, while at the same time conveying the impression of his own insignificance.
The use of natural stone to clad the façades of these, in terms of their construction, very modern buildings merely augmented the monumentality of the architecture.

Top
View across the Great Street, 2 kilometres long and 60 metres wide, to the South, 1938.

Bottom
Speer's Zeppelin Grand stand with central rostrum, completed in 1937.

The "Führer"

The staging of the Party Rally was totally oriented to the "Führer" and the "Führer" myth. The buildings were so designed that they drew the public's attention to the central rostrum from where Hitler spoke. Up to it the "Parteivolk" (loyal Party members) would march, their gaze constantly focused on the "Führer", who was elevated above the masses, their minds symbolically subjugated to his authority.

Light

The "Cathedral of Light" was first staged for the 1936 Olympic Games in Berlin. In Nuremberg during the evening "hour of consecration" of the Political Leaders on the Zeppelin Field it radiated a sacred atmosphere. Over 100 anti-aircraft spotlights positioned around the assembly area produced a building of light as Hitler took his position on the flood-lit Zeppelin Tribune, incidentally modelled on a classical altar, and now bedecked with flags and banners.

Top
Parade in Luitpold Arena, 1934. The so-called "Street of the Führer" constructed from granite slabs, led from the "Führer gallery" to the war memorial.

Right
Rays of the "Cathedral of Light", fire bowls and the illuminated Zeppelin Grandstand, 1937.

Sculptures

Monumental figures and decorations had been commissioned for the buildings and, to some extent, already put in position. Arno Breker and Josef Thorak were the best known of the NS sculptors and the two who received most commissions. They created art for the state, with themes such as the superiority of the German "masterrace", the militarization of society, and the different roles accorded to men and women.

Building Materials

Natural stone played a central role in the NS building programme and for the Party Rally buildings in Nuremberg. Granite, shell limestone, travertine and marble were to increase the aesthetic value of the buildings and underline their permanence. At the same time, natural stone could disguise the industrial character of the building projects and help maintain the idealised view of traditional craft techniques which was of major importance for NS ideology. In June 1939, Hitler decreed that expansion of quarries and stonemasons' companies was to be given priority for the NS building programme. The German Reich had to give them a ten year guarantee for purchasing their fashioned stones. During World War II, natural stone deposits in all occupied countries were checked for their usefulness for the NS building programme.

Top
Excerpt from the so-called "stone placement plan" for the eastern facade of the northern wing of the Congress Hall, 23 November 1938.

Bottom
Group of sculptures by Josef Thorak intended for the main grandstand on the March Field, with the goddess of victory as central figure, 1938.

Forced Labour for the NS-Construction Projects

In June 1934 the SS took control of the approximately 70 concentration camps, which had been set up since the Reichstag fire. They were put under the command of Theodor Eicke, the commandant of Dachau concentration camp, who replaced them with a smaller number of large camps based on the Dachau model. Living conditions in the camps are harsh in the extreme. Armed SS-units guard the outside of the camps; after 1936 they bear the name "Death's Head Units".

At first mainly political prisoners dominated the camps; as of 1936 more and more members of fringe groups and social minorities were interned in the concentration camps. During the war the concentration camp system spread like a festering sore in the form of new satellite and subcamps all over the German occupied countries of Europe. Its function changed dramatically: Not only were prisoners segregated under the severest of imprisonment conditions, they were now totally exploited for the armaments industry. New kinds of camps also arose, in particular, the pure extermination camps and the forced labor camps for Jews, where prisoners were "exterminated by work".

In January 1945 more than 700,000 people representing virtually every nationality in Europe could be found in the regular concentration camps – in contrast to 1939, where the 21,500 prisoners were almost without exception of German or Austrian origin. Owing to the inhuman living and working conditions the death rate was extremely high.

Legend:
- Deutsches Reich
- Grenzen von 1937
- Okkupiertes Gebiet Ende 1941
- Sowjetisches Gebiet unter Militärverwaltung
- Staatsgrenzen
- Gebiets- oder Besatzungsgrenzen
- Konzentrationslager

Map showing main concentration camps in Europe. The camps close to granite quarries – Flossenbürg, Mauthausen, Struthof-Natzweiler and Groß-Rosen – were established in connection with the National Socialists' building projects.

KZ-Labour for the NS Building Programme

Enormous quantities of natural stone and bricks were needed to build the monumental NS structures, and 280 firms provided them. These included the SS-owned German Excavation and Quarrying Works (DEST). Concentration camps such as Flossenbürg, Mauthausen, Groß-Rosen, and Natzweiler-Struthof were set up near stone quarries. There and in the affiliated stonemason firms the DEST mercilessly exploited the labor of the prisoners.

Mauthausen

The granite works of Mauthausen near Linz with its three quarrying firms Wiener Graben, Gusen, and Kastenhof were set up as the only "Level III" concentration camp for "kaum noch erziehbare Schutzhäftlinge" (barely re-educable protective custody inmates). The total number of prisoners was about 190,000 with a maximum of 70,000 by the end of 1944. Approximately 95,000 people died in Mauthausen and its 56 satellite camps.

Flossenbürg

From 1940 Flossenbürg concentration camp (Upper Palatinate) also supplied granite for the buildings then being built in at the Party Rally Grounds. The concentration camp existed from May 1938 until 23 Apri, 1945 and had up to 100 satellite camps in the last few years of the war. At least 30,000 of the more than 100,000 prisoners died.

Top
Inmates carrying stones on the "death stair" in the Mauthausen quarry, no year.

Bottom
Inmates in Flossenbürg concentration camp working on the stone storage square, no year.

Abschrift

4. September 1941
ID/P

An den
Reichsführer SS und Chef der deutschen Polizei,
z. Hd. des SS-Gruppenführer Pohl

Berl.-Lichterfelde-West
Unter den Eichen 127

Betrifft: Granitwerk Natzweiler
              Ihr Schreiben v. 25.7.41 - Amt III A -

Auf Ihr Schreiben vom 25. Juli ds. Jahres teile ich Ihnen mit,
daß unter Bezugnahme auf Ihre fernmündliche Besprechung
mit Herrn Dr. Fränk das rötliche Material aus dem Steinbruch
Natzweiler für das „Deutsche Stadion" in Nürnberg Verwendung
findet. Dieses Bauvorhaben ist in mein Kriegsprogramm
unter der Nr. I Kr St Nürnberg IV aufgenommen worden.

Ich glaube, daß mit der Einreichung dieses Bauvorhabens
in die Dringlichkeitsstufe I auch die Möglichkeit gegeben ist,
die vorbereitenden Arbeiten in Natzweiler zu Ende zu führen.

Das für die Durchführung des Baues benötigte Eisen ist
Ihnen für die ersten drei Quartale zugeteilt worden.
Soweit eine weitere Zuteilung an Eisen für das 4. Quartal notwendig
wird und, sofern eine Zuteilung von Holz notwendig ist,
wäre ich dankbar, wenn Sie mir die notwendigen Mengen
angeben würden.

              Heil Hitler!
              und herzlichen Gruß

              Ihr Speer

In October 1942, Sergej Rybalka, born 23 September, 1925, in Poltawa, Ukraine, was deported by the German Wehrmacht to do forced labour in Germany. After a failed escape attempt in November, the Gestapo took him to the KZ Flossenbürg. On 23 April 1945, the US Army liberated him and other survivors.
The interview was conducted by the Documentation Centre on 5 July, 2000.

Groß-Rosen and Natzweiler-Struthof

Natzweiler-Struthof concentration camp in Alsace and Groß-Rosen in Lower Silesia also provided granite from 1940 on, which was destined, amongst other places, for the Congress Hall and the German Stadium. A major consideration behind the location of Natzweiler-Struthof concentration camp was its proximity to the occurrence of an unusually red granite, which was intended for the German Stadium in Nuremberg.

Interview with eye-witness Sergej Rybalka

"The stones that we worked were sent afterwards in the 'Galle' (stonemason barracks) to the stonemasons. When the trucks came to pick them up, we helped load them up. They were transported to various cities, including Nuremberg. Beautiful stones, well cut, like, for example, marble, 1 meter, 1 meter fifty cm, or 2 meters long. I remember one driver well who came from Nuremberg. His name was Max … 'Where are you going, Max?' we asked. 'To Nuremberg', he said.

Here is where the daily harassment took place. I must honestly say that not one of us prisoners did any harm to anyone. This is where the half-dead people were brought down from the hill and driven to the camp. There was a lot of sadism. Many were injured by falling stones or killed. No safety measures were observed, no medical aid given. Every day was the same. The men quarried the stones here, half-clothed, with wooden shoes which made your feet bleed, without gloves. This damned hill! How many human lives, how much energy this hill swallowed up! I can't even find the right expression. The stones were good, but for what price were they produced. For hundreds and thousands of human lives. And the people who worked here were paid nothing. The thought of getting money never crossed their minds. They worked for a plate of thin soup and rotten potatoes; after work they were allowed to go back to the camp. The next morning it started all over again, it just kept being repeated."

Top
Letter from the Plenipotentiary for Building Management, Albert Speer, concerning the extension of the Struthof-Natzweiler concentration camp.

Bottom right
Inmates of the Flossenbürg concentration camp receiving food.

The Party Rallies as Ritual

The Party Rallies were used for the self-promotion of the Party, both at home and abroad, staging the "Volksgemeinschaft" and the "Führer" myth. Parades, the ubiquitous presence of uniforms and military displays were immediately linked to war preparations made by the NS state.

But mainly the Party Rallies addressed the emotions of both participants and spectators. Politics were not to be understood, but to be "experienced". The staged presentations became the new political message. After 1933, the Party Rallies were more or less conducted with the same ritual: mass parades, military displays, speeches, meetings of NS organisations, propaganda exhibitions, funfairs, fireworks, as well as concerts and opera productions made up the programme.

When presenting itself thus, the NSDAP made use of many traditions: Christian and supposedly German rites, as well as military rituals, elements of bourgeois celebratory culture, forms of political expression of the workers' movement or of the Italian Fascist movement.

1936 Party Rally poster.

After 1933, the Party Rallies were given a different title every year. In the year of the "Seizure of Power", the Nazis celebrated the "Party Rally of Victory", in 1934, 1935 and 1936, the Party Rallies of "Unity and Strength", "Liberty" and "Honour" were held, followed by the 1937 Party Rally of "Labour" and 1938 Party Rally of "Greater Germany". Because the German Reich attacked Poland on 1 September, 1939, the Party Rally scheduled for September was cancelled. It would have been the "Party Rally of Peace".

The Party Rallies lasted five days in 1933, seven after 1934 and eight days from 1937. Every day had a specific motto. Up to one million people came to Nuremberg every year for the Party Rallies. Only few of them noticed the subliminal violence beneath the fascination generated by the skilful party rally stage management.

"The Day of Welcome"

It was Hitler himself who marked the start of the annual Nazi Party Rallies: He arrived in the afternoon at the main train station in Nuremberg. The city afforded him a large reception at the Town Hall. The cultural highlight was the gala performance of Richard Wagner's The Mastersingers of Nuremberg at the Opera House.

"The Opening Day of the Congress"

In the morning hours of the second day the participants in the "Adolf Hitler March" paraded past Hitler's rooms in the Deutscher Hof hotel. This followed the actual opening of the Party Rallies with the Party Congress in the Luitpold Hall. The agenda of these events was also ritualized, a mixture of liturgical service and court ceremony. The day closed with the Cultural Conference in the Opera House and the awarding of the "German National Prize for Art and Science".

Top right
Hitler walking past a Wehrmacht guard of honour in front of Nuremberg City Hall, on 6 September, 1937. This is where the official reception honouring the "Führer" was held.

Bottom
Gauleiter Julius Streicher during his welcoming speech at the NSDAP Party Congress in Luitpold Hall with a capacity audience of 16,000 party members on 5 September, 1934.

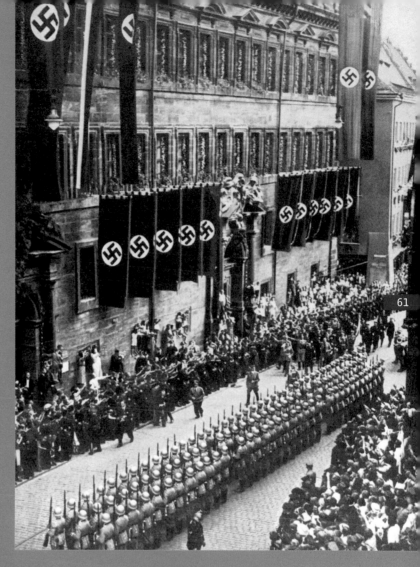

"The Day of the Reich Labor Service"

In the morning the Reich Labor Service (RAD) opened up the round of large parades. 45,000 men lined up in formation on the Zeppelin Field after marching past the main tribune. This was followed by a ceremony with pseudo-religious character, again with a remembrance ceremony for the dead, with melodic chants and prayers of thanksgiving. In the evening several tens of thousands of Political Leaders – the party officials – marched in a torchlight parade past Hitler at the Deutscher Hof.

"The Day of the Community"

In 1937 the Party Rally was extended by an eighth day, the "Day of the Community". It offered the public a series of seemingly apolitical and entertaining sports events: mass gymnastics exercises and dance performances on the Zeppelin Field or the military sporting events of the NS, such as swimming in uniform or hand-grenade-throwing events in the municipal sports stadium. Most of these NS sports competitions took place on the "Day of the Community". From 1937 onwards the torchlight parade of the Political Leaders also took place on this day.

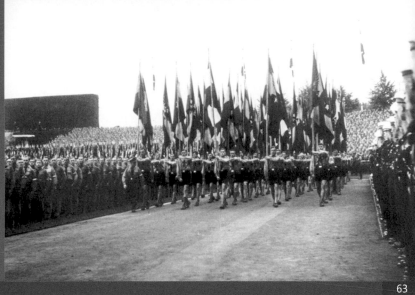

"The Day of the Political Leaders"

After a parade of police units in the morning, special conferences characterized the day's agenda, including the afternoon conference of the NS Women's Organizations. The high point of the day was the evening roll call of the Political Leaders. A sophisticated system of lighting, as of 1936 the staging of the cathedral of light created from the beams of over a hundred spotlights, embellished an evening hour of consecration, with flag parades and prayers of thanksgiving.

"The Day of the Hitler Youth"

The main event on this day was the Hitler Youth ceremony. Approximately 50,000 young men entered the municipal stadium. Here, too, the ceremony was marked by the entry of the flags, songs, and the declaration of belief in the Führer. The climax was when, at the end, Hitler walked past the young people giving them the feeling of having "personally encountered" the Führer.

Top left to right

March-in of the RAD (German Labour Service) units on Zeppelin Field, 12 September, 1935. The Labour Service was not part of the NSDAP.

Participants of the Bund Deutscher Mädel (BDM Association of German Girls) during dance displays on Zeppelin Field, 8 September, 1938.

Torch parade of the Political Leaders (office bearers of the NSDAP), 8 September, 1938. After assembling on Deutschherrnwiese, the Political Leaders marched to the "Deutscher Hof" hotel for a parade in front of Hitler.

Entrance of Hitler Youth flag bearers in the Municipal Stadium, 11 September, 1937. In that year, 45,000 boys from the Hitler Youth and 5,000 girls from the BDM took part in the event.

Bottom left
Competition in hand grenade throwing on targets in the Municipal Stadium, 1937. Most of the competitions of the "NS Sports Competitions" took place during the "Day of the Community".

Bottom right
Spectators had to pay for everything: Ticket for the roll-call of the political leaders on the Zeppelin Field, 1937.

"The Day of the SA and the SS"

The culmination of the Party Rallies was the roll-call of about 100,000 Party soldiers on "The Day of the SA and the SS" in the Luitpoldhain. Once again there was a community experience for everyone, consisting of, among other things, the remembrance of the dead and oath of mutual loyalty, the singing of songs, and the consecration of new flags with the so-called "Blood Flag". This was followed by a parade through the city, lasting hours, which went past Hitler who inspected the parade at the main market square. The loyal party members dominated the scene and were present throughout the city from morning to night.

"The Day of the Wehrmacht"

The Party Rally closed with a display of Wehrmacht maneuvers on the Zeppelin Field on the "Day of the Wehrmacht". Owing to the large number of visitors, there was one demonstration in the morning and one in the afternoon. Hitler and other prominent spectators were present at the latter, watching the loudly cheered field maneuvers and the final parade march past the main tribune. The final rally in the Luitpold Hall as well as an evening tattoo in front of the Deutscher Hof hotel ended the one-week spectacle.

Top left
Consecration of flags during the roll-call of the SA and SS in Luitpold Arena, 13 September 1936. Hitler "consecrates" new standards by touching them with the "blood flag", supposedly one of the flags carried during the putsch of 9 November 1923, and bespattered with blood.

Top right
The face of war: soldiers from motorised Wehrmacht units wearing gas masks on the "Day of the Wehrmacht", on Zeppelin Field, 12 September 1938.

The National Socialist Calendar of Public Holidays

The Party Rallies were not the only lavish event in the regime's calendar of image-fostering celebrations. They did represent though the culmination of an entire National Socialist calendar of public holidays, including: The Day of the Seizure of Power (January 30), Foundation Day of the NSDAP (24 February), Veterans' Day (March), Hitler's Birthday (20 April), National Labor Day (1 May), Mothering Sunday (May), Summer Solstice Day (June), Nazi Party Rallies (September), Harvest Thanksgiving Day (October), Remembrance Day for those who died 1923 in the Beer-Hall Putsch (9 November), Volksweihnacht (Christmas Eve, 24 December). This cycle of public holidays was originally intended first to complement the calendar of church festivals, and then later to replace it altogether.

Top left
Memorial day for the "Dead of the Movement".
Flanked by SA and SS formations, Hitler walks towards the two "Temples of Honour" on Munich Königsplatz.

Top right
Ticket for the fireworks, 1935.

Bottom
Dress rehearsal of the SA for the Summer Solstice celebration in the Berlin Olympic Stadium, about 1936.

The Organization of the Nazi Party Rallies

The NSDAP organizational department managed the agenda of the Nazi Party Rallies. It issued instructions to the Party Rally Department of the City of Nuremberg. This department, in turn, allotted the organizational tasks, such as transport, lodging and feeding of participants, traffic control, and parade planning, to the other municipal offices. Nothing was left to chance: The Party Rally Department was also responsible for the city's ceremonial decorations and the official reception for the Führer at the Town Hall.

The NSDAP members had to make a special contribution towards the financing of the Nazi Party Rallies. Admission fees were also charged for attendance at the events.

Top
Marching plan for the SA and SS in the
Luitpold Arena, 1936.

Bottom
Ticket for the roll-call in the Luitpold Arena
on the "Day of the SA and SS", 1937.

67

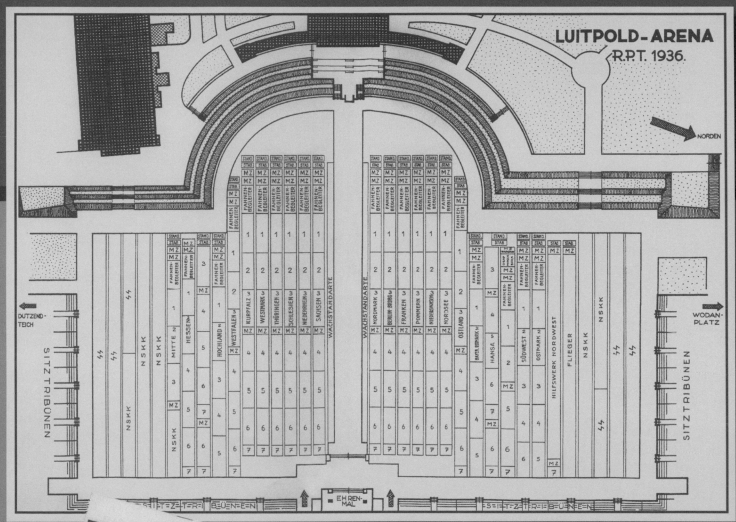

Top
Roll-Call in the Luitpold Arena, 1933.

Left
The "Party Rally Chair", a folding chair
which sold cheap to spectators, 1930s.

Right
Flow chart for transport and events
during the 1936 Party Rally.

Bottom right
Ticket for the show manoevre
of the Wehrmacht, 1935.

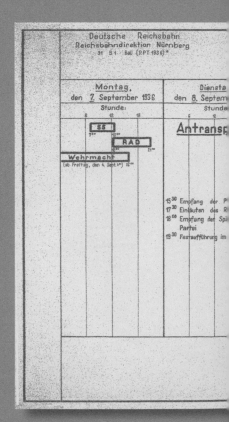

Deutsche Reichsbahn
Reichsbahndirektion Nürnberg
31 51. Baü (RPT 1936)*

Montag,
den 7. September 1936
Stunde:

Diensta
den 8. Septem
Stunde

SS

RAD

Antransp

Wehrmacht
(ab Freitag, den 4. Sept 36)

15³⁰ Empfang der Pl
17³⁰ Einläuten des Ri
18⁰⁰ Empfang der Spi
Partei
19³⁰ Festaufführung im

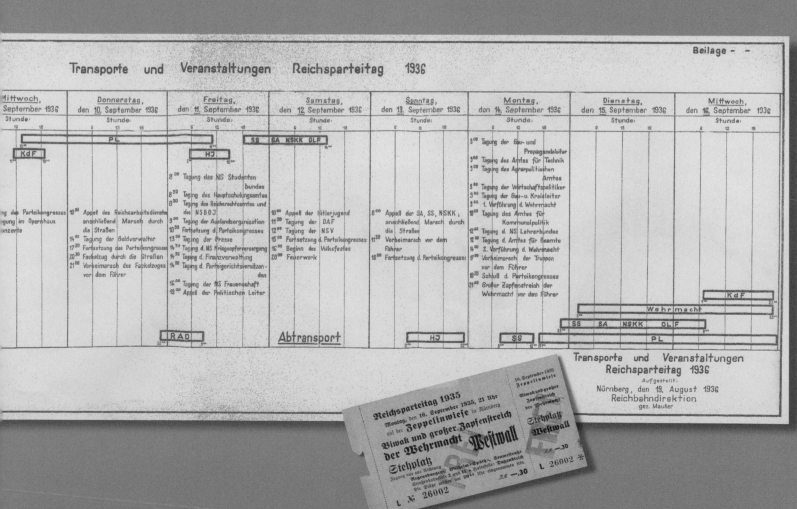

Beilage - -

Transporte und Veranstaltungen Reichsparteitag 1936

Mittwoch, September 1936	Donnerstag, den 10. September 1936	Freitag, den 11. September 1936	Samstag, den 12. September 1936	Sonntag, den 13. September 1936	Montag, den 14. September 1936	Dienstag, den 15. September 1936	Mittwoch, den 16. September 1936

Donnerstag:
10⁰⁰ Appell des Reichsarbeitsdienstes anschließend Marsch durch die Straßen
14⁰⁰ Tagung der Geldverwalter
17⁰⁰ Fortsetzung des Parteikongresses
20³⁰ Fackelzug durch die Straßen
21⁰⁰ Vorbeimarsch des Fackelzuges vor dem Führer

Freitag:
8⁰⁰ Tagung des NS Studentenbundes
8³⁰ Tagung des Hauptschulungsamtes
8³⁰ Tagung des Reichsrechtsamtes und des NSBDJ
9⁰⁰ Tagung der Auslandsorganisation
10³⁰ Fortsetzung d. Parteikongresses
13⁰⁰ Tagung der Presse
14³⁰ Tagung d. NS Kriegsopferversorgung
14³⁰ Tagung d. Finanzverwaltung
14³⁰ Tagung d. Parteigerichtsvorsitzenden
16⁰⁰ Tagung der NS Frauenschaft
19⁰⁰ Appell der Politischen Leiter

Samstag:
10⁰⁰ Appell der Hitlerjugend
11³⁰ Tagung der DAF
12⁰⁰ Tagung der NSV
15⁰⁰ Fortsetzung d. Parteikongresses
16⁰⁰ Beginn des Volksfestes
20⁰⁰ Feuerwerk

Sonntag:
8⁰⁰ Appell der SA, SS, NSKK; anschließend Marsch durch die Straßen
11³⁰ Vorbeimarsch vor dem Führer
18⁰⁰ Fortsetzung d. Parteikongresses

Montag:
8⁰⁰ Tagung der Gau- und Propagandaleiter
9⁰⁰ Tagung des Amtes für Technik
9⁰⁰ Tagung des Agrarpolitischen Amtes
9⁰⁰ Tagung der Wirtschaftspolitiker
9⁰⁰ Tagung der Gau- u. Kreisleiter
10⁰⁰ 1. Vorführung d. Wehrmacht
10⁰⁰ Tagung des Amtes für Kommunalpolitik
12⁰⁰ Tagung d. NS Lehrerbundes
12⁰⁰ Tagung d. Amtes für Beamte
14⁰⁰ 2. Vorführung d. Wehrmacht
17⁰⁰ Vorbeimarsch der Truppen vor dem Führer
19⁰⁰ Schluß d. Parteikongresses
21⁰⁰ Großer Zapfenstreich der Wehrmacht vor dem Führer

Transporte und Veranstaltungen Reichsparteitag 1936
Aufgestellt:
Nürnberg, den 19. August 1936
Reichsbahndirektion
gez. Maußer

The Event of the Nazi Party Rallies

The organizers of the Nazi Party Rallies were aiming at the highest number possible of participants and visitors to demonstrate that the NS regime had become firmly embedded within the population. All the organizations of the NSDAP were represented in Nuremberg. Many of the visitors came of their own initiative. Participants from the ranks of the SA and SS, the Reichsarbeitsdienst (RAD, Reich Labor Service), the Hitler-Jugend (HJ, Hitler Youth), the Bund Deutscher Mädel (BDM, League of German Girls) and the Wehrmacht were selected according to National Socialist ethnic criteria.

Along with the official participants came hundreds of thousands of visitors. They streamed as spectators to the Party Rallies, experienced the hustle and bustle in the Old Town or enjoyed the pleasures of the Volksfest (fun fair). The Party Rally Grounds as well as the marches and roll calls were great attractions – and many a souvenir photo was taken to capture the atmosphere of the occasion.

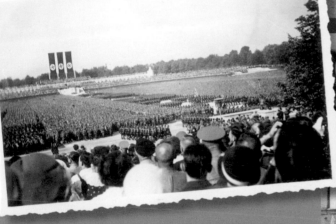

Top left
Parade on the "Day of the SA and SS" in Luitpold Grove seen from the spectators' perspective, 1934.

Bottom left
Souvenir beer mug from "Nuremberg – City of the Party Rallies", 1930s.

Top right
From 1935, the Reich management of the Hitler Youth organised the "Adolf Hitler March of the German Youth" with about 2,000 carefully selected 16-to-20-year-olds. A HJ marching delegation is welcomed on the outskirts, 1937.

Bottom right
Party rally participants from Cologne arriving at Nuremberg station, 1933.

The Party Rallies in Colour

As colour photography was still expensive and thus not too common in those days comparably few colour photos of the party rallies exist. Nearly all of these pictures on pages 68–71 were made by an Austrian spectator visiting the party rally in 1938. The picture on page 70 (above left) stems from the official report published by the NSDAP.

The Königstrasse in the City in full colour.

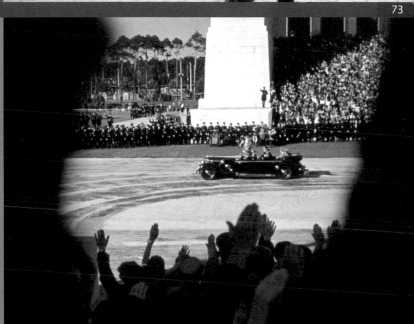

Top left
Hitler on the balcony of Deutscher Hof hotel.

Top right
Crowds strolling in front of the castle.

Bottom left
Spectators entering the tribunes of the
Luitpold Arena.

Bottom right
Spectator's view on Hitler passing by in his
car before the Zeppelin Grand Stand.

Top left
Standard bearers during the roll-call
in the Luitpold Arena, 1938.

Top right and bottom
Scenes from the "Day of the Community"
on the Zeppelin Field.

Roll-call of the SA and SS
in the Luitpold Arena.

National Socialist propaganda always emphasized the enthusiasm of the Party Rally participants, spectators, and visitors. Yet the technically brilliant propaganda films and the official reports convey only the shiny façade of the mass propaganda spectacle. Numerous internal memoranda of the NSDAP organizational leadership and the Nuremberg municipal administration reveal the sharp contrast between the desire to orchestrate a perfect performance and the reality of numerous organizational inadequacies.

Top
Visitors walking through the Luitpold Arena covered in rubbish, where many participants waited for more than half a day and took part in a roll-call, 1934.

Bottom
Straw beds for political leaders in a Nuremberg factory hall, 1933.

Ideal and Reality

"The torchlight parade of the Political Leaders was nothing less than a disaster. Most of the Political Leaders were totally unaware that they had marched past the Führer. Pushing people on all the time and the non-stop marching that we see year after year causes total confusion. Only a very few Gaus (Nazi political/territorial division) presented a fairly unified line. It is completely unthinkable to let the Gaus march without any distance between them. It was, in plain and simple German – embarrassing."
(Report: Reference: Torchlight Parade – Party Rally of 1938)

"Experience gained at the Nazi Party Rallies in 1933 and 1934 led to the Nuremberg red light district also being cordoned off during the Nazi Party Rally of 1935. As in the past, these streets, in which approximately 120 wage-earning prostitutes live next to each other in individual houses, were the goal of a good many visitors during the week of the Rallies. Above all, one couldn't help observing that the P.O.-Männer (Political Leaders), who enjoy more freedom of movement than others during the Rallies, repeatedly try to get into these streets despite the latter being conspicuously cordoned off by SS guards day and night."
(Report by the vice squad on the Nazi Party Rally of 1935, 28 November, 1935)

"Magdeburg-Anhalt: the camp site allotted to our gau was in Moorenbrunn – the name says a lot – was so damp that even after short downpours, the water was streaming into the tents. Only by digging ditches the tents of my political leaders could be kept dry during rain. Roll-calls on the camp site were sometimes impossible due to wetness and mud."
(Report: re accommodation 1938 Party Rally)

The Gau Koblenz-Trier in the Flurstraße was a disaster area, describing it as a "pig sty" is still putting it too mildly. Not only the fact that the Political Leaders who'd occupied these rooms had left behind all sorts of paper and cardboard boxes, but in every corner there were remains of old food, sausages and cheese, cigar and cigarette butts as well as other kinds of refuse which stank so much that you felt sick when you entered the rooms."
(Report about the revision of the quarters occupied by the Political leaders during the Nazi Party Rally 1936)

Eye witnesses remember

Arno Hamburger, head of the Jewish Congregation, left Nuremberg in 1939 and went to Palestine. In May 1945, he returned here as an English soldier.

Arno Hamburger (1923–2013)

"It was always particularly difficult for us during the Party Rallies. On the one hand these rallies were usually during our High Holidays, that is [Jewish] New Year and Yom Kippur. We youths, we children used to move back and forth between the two synagogues, we did that an awful lot, that is between the synagogue on Hans Sachs square and the synagogue in the Essenweinstraße. And one of the main meeting points, the focal point, was the Deutscher Hof, where Hitler stayed. It lay exactly on the way from the Hans Sachs square to the Essenweinstraße. And when we pushed our way through the crowd there, with our prayer books, that was some adventure, because we knew exactly that if we were caught with a Jewish prayer book tucked under our arms, all hell would be set loose! You did try very hard to keep away from the streets during the parades, because you were obliged to greet the swastika flag. You had two choices: either you did not lift your hand, then you were shouted at by the people around you. Or you lifted your hand and were recognised as a Jew, and that was even worse."

Käthe Fettahoglu during her eyewitness interview in 2000.

Käthe Fettahoglu (*1923)

"For me the Party Rallies were just about as important as Christmas. My friends and I had a kind of competition: Who could see the Führer the most times. In 1937 I saw him twelve times, and in 1938 thirteen times. And we also made our way to the Deutscher Hof, usually at least, and didn't simply call out "We want to see our Führer!", but used to chant things like: "Dearest Führer, be so kind, come to the window, no one will mind!" And can also remember seeing that he sometimes smiled a little when he came out and even greeted us. My father had given us two painters' ladders and a long board and the uncles had carted the ladders and the board over to the southwest corner of the Town Hall. People were standing five and six rows deep, so that if you were a normal size, you couldn't see anything. Then we set up our ladders and laid the board between them at the top and my two aunts and I stood on top of the board and the others on the rungs of the ladder and we also had a couple of small folding chairs, which we'd bought extra for the Party Rallies (the so-called "Party Rally Chair"). And that's where we waited."

Using an umbrella, Reinhold Schwiddesen in 2000 demonstrated how the spade had to be presented. This move performed by 50,000 members of the Reich Labour Force much impressed the spectators.

Reinhold Schwiddesen (*1919)

"There was a community feeling, they like parades, and to be given an award on Sundays because you could march well – that was a real experience. Yes, only especially selected people were allowed in. If we had been pulled aside afterwards, because we had marched worse than the others, then we would have cried our hearts out, I'm sure of it."

The Response Abroad

There was great concern within the NS regime, especially in the first few years, that decisions taken elicited the right response from abroad. Hitler and his followers knew their goals could be jeopardized by the reactions of foreign governments. National Socialist policy-making therefore choose a mixture of the offensive and the defensive as the best approach, of barely concealed threats and simultaneous assertions of peace.

Nuremberg's role was above all to clearly demonstrate the substantial approval of National Socialism among the German people. However, the absence of official foreign representatives, of diplomats, and ambassadors left a great deal to be desired in the first few years. Great Britain and France did not send their ambassadors to Nuremberg until 1937. The United States waited until a year later.

The echo in the foreign press also remained divided. The democratic states of Europe and North America criticized the resurgence of militarism expressed in Nuremberg as well as the unrestrained use of the propaganda machine. The press reports in the countries ruled by dictatorships or authoritarian governments, such as Italy, the Soviet Union, or Austria reflected only their respective relations with the Third Reich.

Les Maitres-Chanteurs de Nuremberg. (Reprise.)

France

The comments of the French press varied enormously, depending on the political leanings of the respective papers. They ranged from the assessment of the Party Rallies by the Communist newspaper "L'Humanité" as purely a propaganda spectacle to a clearly sympathetic stance in the right-wing weekly "L'Illustration".

"I do not believe that within living memory there has been a spectacle that could compare to this in size and in beauty – National Socialism, which is often found wanting in spirit and intellect, has found its genius. With the aesthetics of this stage production it now supplements its cultural heritage. What used to be action and activity has now become a ritual. Such is the history of each religion, thus also of the National Socialist religion."
L'Echo de Paris, 9 September 1934

"After the fever of Fascist hysterics has reached its maximum, Hitler's troops have returned to their regions. The Congress was dominated by more or less implausible and deceptive speeches delivered by the bosses, the party basis and the youth did not have a say (...) These bandits who cannot guarantee basic supplies to their people, now offer their troops who are livid with rage anti-Semitic pogroms!"
L'Humanité, 4 September 1933

Great Britain

British newspapers, particularly the "Times", usually had their own correspondents on site during the Party Rallies. The spectacular orchestration of the events elicited respect even from liberal and leftwing papers. Yet at the same time the press criticized the absence of freedom of speech in Germany and exposed NS propaganda as well as the emotionalization of the masses as instruments for securing domination and control over the people.

"Three hundred and fiftyseven trains are bringing the forces of National Socialism from every part of Germany to this city of medieval houses, which was great when Berlin was but a village, for the first congress of the National Socialist party since Herr Hitler became absolute master of Germany.

Everywhere in streets and hotels and cafés are leaders and organisers who wear brown uniforms cut exactly like those of British officers in wartime. They salute by raising the right arm in the Italian manner, saying 'Heil Hitler!' in the sharp tone of a military command."
The Daily Mail, September 1933

THE RIVAL MASTERSINGERS OF NUREMBERG

Top
Cartoon "The Master Singers of Nuremberg" (Repeat Performance) in "L'Oeuvre" of 7 September, 1938.
Bottom
"The Rival Mastersingers of Nuremberg"
Cartoon in the "Daily Express", 6 September, 1934.

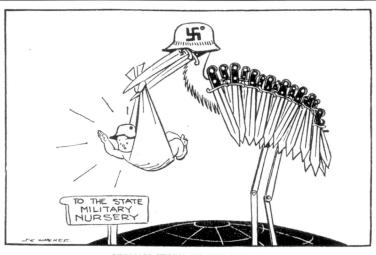

GERMAN STORK OF THE FUTURE

TO THE STATE MILITARY NURSERY

Soviet Union

The state-controlled Soviet press condemned the Party Rallies from the very beginning and in the sharpest possible terms. In its opinion the events served only to demonize Communism publicly and to declare it the arch-enemy of German culture. Moreover, it was clearly expressed in the newspapers that the Soviet Union was the major target of National Socialist plans for territorial expansion.

"The organisers of the concentration camps, barbarians who have lost their human face will be talking about protecting civilisation. Thugs who burn books and ban verses by Goethe and Schiller from German school readers, will be talking about culture."
Pravda, 6 September 1936

"Endless drill until they almost faint, incessant bawling which is supposed to be "enthusiasm", cheap trinkets, flashy decorations, rampant, almost hysterical anti-Soviet screaming – all this nonsense follows a specific goal. It makes sure that people don't have time for reflection. Incite their passion – that is the motto behind the Nuremberg bacchanalia of bloody war mongers."
Izvestija, 16 September 1936

USA

The correspondents of the major American newspapers observed the Party Rallies with skepticism. They described not only the pompous exterior of the events, but also the manipulation of the masses associated with it and condemned the cult of violence encouraged in Nuremberg. As early as 1933 a few newspapers had come to the conclusion that the NS dictatorship was a threat to world peace.

"The young Germany is showing its strength. And young Germany is very strong."
New York Times, 4 September, 1933

"Sacrilegious though it may seem, Germany of today can be explained to the foreigner only if he is made to realize that the great German nation has a Messiah-complex and that Hitler is the incarnation of their hopes for better days."
Chicago Daily News, 10 September, 1934

Czechoslovakia

Czechoslovakian newspapers reported extensively on the Party Rallies, disapproving to hostile in their stance. Even before the Sudeten crisis of 1938 the press recognized the danger for their own country emanating from the National Socialist policy of territorial expansion. The polemical caricatures of the Party Rallies published in the daily newspapers "Lidové Noviny" and "Rudé Právo" were particularly striking.

"It was not a party rally in the usual sense. As was to be expected, there was no debate, no discussion. There were only proclamations."
Prager Presse, looking back on the 1933 Party Rally, title page

"... that certain groups can hardly wait until it's no longer just manoeuvres, but real war. And while Germany provocatively boasts that it owns all prohibited weapons and even displays them to diplomats and soldiers, Hitler has the courage to talk about peace."
Pravo Lidu, 11 September, 1934

„Und hier sehen Sie Deutschlands älteste Kulturkammer!"

Austria

The Austrian government was exposed to German threats immediately after the "Seizure of Power". Accordingly, the relationship between the two countries was bad; open criticism of the Third Reich posed a risk for the small country. A good many Austrian newspapers therefore tried to ignore the Party Rallies as well as they could; others voiced clear criticism, at least at the beginning. In 1933 the authoritarian Austrian leadership, with the help of the press, began staging its own festivities as a clear counterstatement to Nuremberg.

"The Party Rally of the German Nazis in Nuremberg, after festive drum rolls and flag waving, started with truly sensational confessions of the absolute inability of the Hitler regime to fight effectively against the imminent collapse of the German economy and to achieve even the slightest improvement. This was not only a declaration of bankruptcy of the brown-shirts, that all their boastful promises had been nothing but lies and deceit – it was a true alarm call going out into the world from Hitler's Party Rally".
Arbeiter-Zeitung, 1 September, 1933

Italy

In Fascist Italy the press followed the guidelines laid down by the government. It was only after 1936, as Italy drew closer to the Third Reich, that reports on the Party Rallies took up more space in the newspapers. The reports praised the organization of the events and the military demonstrations as an expression of the "new, strong Germany". On the other hand, the "Nuremberg Laws" passed in 1935 found no mention at all.

"All this has awakened Germany, a new German mentality which has made such aggressive and belligerent noises during the last Party Rally in Nuremberg."
Illustrazione Italiana, 3 September, 1936

"The tenth meeting of the Swastika movement was a full, undisputed success of superb organisation, which has had to deal with more difficult and bigger tasks every year. The success of the Führer was also incredible, with the German people trusting him more and more strongly and expressing.its willingness to follow him, even in difficult times."
Il Messagero, 12 September, 1938

Left
"German Stork of the Future"
Cartoon in the „Western Mail and South Wales News", no date.

Right
"… and here you see Germany's oldest Chamber of Culture".
Contemporary caricature from Austria, no date.

"Triumph of the Will"

In April 1934 Adolf Hitler commissioned the dancer, actress and director Leni Riefenstahl with the making of a film about the "Party Rally of Unity and Strength" which was to take place in September of the same year. Already a year ago she had produced a film about the "Party Rally of Victory" which showed many deficiencies in its design and dramaturgy. Also it showed the leader of the SA, Ernst Röhm, on equal footing with Hitler. Röhm was murdered by Hitler's order in a "night of the long knives" due to conflicting power interests.

"Triumph of the Will" – Hitler himself gave it the title – was a most perfect arranged propaganda film of two hours length. After its premiere on 28 March, 1935, in the Berlin UFA Palace, the film was shown in 70 German cities. The NSDAP film lending service used it for political education purposes and showed it in schools. Viewing was compulsory for school students.

This exceptionally well-structured and masterly deceptive film was created with state-of-the-art film techniques, unusual camera angles and in months of editing in post-production. The film was to become the basis for any visual memory of the party rallies with their stage-managed masses and transported their most important message: the link between the "Führer" and "his people". Hitler figures in person in a third of the film. After the end of the war in 1945, the victorious allied powers prohibited public screenings of this propaganda film.

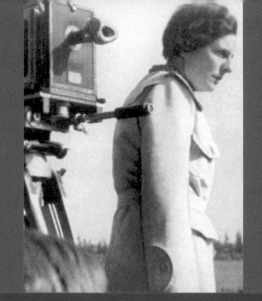

"I designed the film in such a way that it will rouse its audiences, uplifting them more and more from act to act, from impression to impression."

Leni Riefenstahl

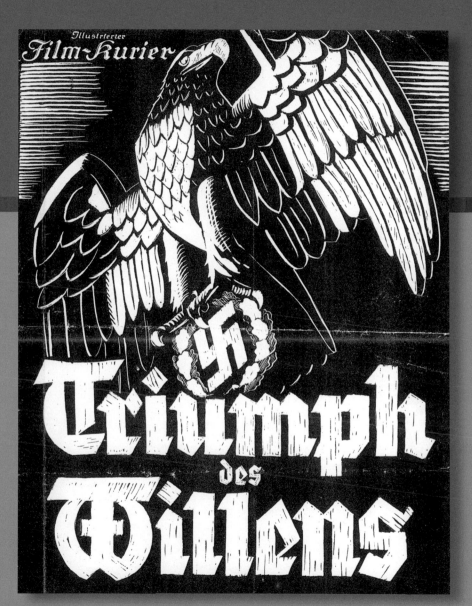

Top
Leni Riefenstahl during the making of "Triumph of the Will", Nuremberg, 1934.

Bottom
Title page of the "Illustrated Film Courier", 1935. The film was honoured with highest international awards: "Best Foreign Documentary" at the 1935 Venice International Film Festival; gold medal with diploma during the 1937 World Exhibition in Paris.

84

"*In Nuremberg, it was 'Franconian Führer', Streicher, who overcame many difficulties for us. The novel use of all technical means for the film was supported in particular by the City of Nuremberg. All technical aids we needed, right through to tram cars and fireman's ladders, were provided to us by Lord Mayor Liebel.*"

Leni Riefenstahl

For filming in Luitpold Grove, a lifting mechanism was attached to one of the flag poles. This enabled vertical camera drives, with an unusual view of the masses gathered here.

Leni Riefenstahl and her crew during a production meeting. Her production crew comprised 170 persons. She used 16 of the best camera operators of the time.

The director tried to counteract the boring party rally speeches with unusual camera moves. During the appeal to the German youth in the municipal stadium, she went round Hitler on a circle of rails. By viewing the speaker from below, she raised him to the status of a living memorial.

"Two million people can gather in Nuremberg, the City of the Party Rallies. 60 million Germans must witness this gigantic parade (...) Above all of this it was the close link between the "Führer" and his people which was the major experience over and over again. One of the main tasks I set for myself is expressing this feeling."

Leni Riefenstahl

Racism and Anti-Semitism

Anti-Semitism has a long tradition. Although not restricted to Germany, it was here that National Socialism radicalized the hatred of Jews; this hatred was popularized by forceful slogans and – for the first time in history – raised to state doctrine. Racism, an ideological waste product of a pseudo-scientific explanation of the world, divided people into races of different worth, into "creative and destructive" races.

In so doing it incorporates the idea that mankind, peoples, and races were caught up by the laws of nature in a perpetual struggle for survival, in which the "weak" and "ill" elements would be eradicated by the "strong" and "healthy" elements.

This body of thought held the Jews to be a parasitic people, seeking to destroy from within the peoples of "the greatest value". After the October Revolution of 1917 in Russia it was coupled with another idea – that Bolshevism was an instrument of the Jews in their struggle to dominate the world. The "Jewish-Bolshevist Enemy" was born.

The victims of racial persecution in the Third Reich were not only Jews, but also Sinti and Roma, called "gypsies". However, racism was also directed against "one's own race": Those classified as having an inferior genetic make-up should be expelled from the "genetic bloodline" of the German people; so-called life unworthy of life should be exterminated.

The war finally removed all inhibitions about a "biological" solution to alleged biological problems. Organized acts of murder on a limited scale escalated into "elimination" campaigns and – in the fall of 1941 – these, in turn, became systematic genocide.

The "Nuremberg Laws" – Origin

The great "highlight" at the end of the "Party Rally of Freedom" in 1935 was the convening of the German Reichstag in Nuremberg. It had planned to pass a Reich Flag Law that would make the swastika flag a Reich and war flag. Tactical considerations and prevailing sentiments influenced Hitler to introduce two further laws to the Reichstag, which had been under discussion for some time: A state citizenship law for Jews and a "racial segregation law". The "Reich Citizenship Law" and a "Law for the Protection of German Blood and Honor" soon became well known as the "Nuremberg Laws".

Top left
Göring, president of the Reichstag (centre), reads out the text of the "Nuremberg Laws" to the members of the Reichstag assembled in the Nuremberg Kulturvereinssaal, on 15 September, 1935.

Right
The "Law for the Protection of German Blood" of 15 September, 1935. In 1936, a decree issued by the Reich Ministry of the Interior also subjected Sinti and Roma and coloured people to the "Blood Protection Law".

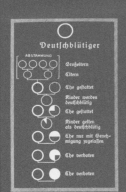

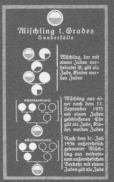

Die Nürnberger Gesetze in Übersichtstafeln

Das Reichsbürgerrecht ist in jedem einzelnen Falle von der Verleihung abhängig

Bestehende Ehen bleiben unberührt

Zeichenerklärung

Deutschblütiger — gehört der deutschen Bluts- und Volksgemeinschaft an, kann Reichsbürger werden

Mischling 2. Grades — gehört nur der deutschen Volksgemeinschaft an, kann Reichsbürger werden

Mischling 1. Grades — gehört nur der deutschen Volksgemeinschaft an, kann Reichsbürger werden

Jude — gehört der jüdischen Bluts- und Volksgemeinschaft an, kann nicht Reichsbürger werden

Jude — gehört der jüdischen Bluts- und Volksgemeinschaft an, kann nicht Reichsbürger werden

The "Nuremberg Laws" – Contents

The Reich Citizenship Law granted a new Reich Citizenship, with "full political rights", to all subjects with "German or kindred blood". Jews, who were simply subjects of the state, were degraded to second-class citizens. The "Law for the Protection of German Blood and Honor" forbade marriages between Germans and Jews and made extra-marital relationships between them punishable by prison, whereby it was the man who was to be punished. A Jew was defined as an individual descended from four or three full-Jewish grandparents ("full and three-quarter Jews"). Only in certain cases was a Jew an individual with two full-Jewish grandparents ("half-Jews").

Graphic representation of the marriages prohibited by the "Blood Protection Law".

The "Nuremberg Laws" – Purpose and Consequences

Prior to the "Nuremberg Laws" there had been a wave of violent attacks against men and women accused of alleged "race-defiling" relationships. The Laws bestowed "legality" on this terror. For Hitler the Laws were just an interim step along the road to a much more comprehensive solution. They accelerated the social isolation of the Jews: Anyone who had contact with Jews exposed himself to suspicions of "political unreliability" or even "race defilement". The Reich Citizenship Law opened up for the Gestapo new and broader fields of activity: the prosecution of socalled racial offenses. The Reich Citizenship Law was followed by 13 supplementary decrees, through which the Jews were, step by step, totally stripped of their rights – even to the point of being later expatriated through deportation to the East.

Anti-Semitism in the Daily Life of the Third Reich

Anti-Semitism was universally present in the daily life of the Third Reich: in the press, the radio, films, in political education taking place at clubs and organizations, at schools. Even the youngest of children were indoctrinated with a hatred of Jews. Amongst the most ruthless and aggressive of the anti-Semites was the "Franconian Führer" Julius Streicher. The coarse and primitive contents of "Der Stürmer", the rabble-rousing newspaper published by Streicher since 1923, the books printed by the Nuremberg Stürmer press, and the announcements in the so-called "Stürmer-showcases" gave rise to repeated protests.

Left
Public humiliation of "offenders who defiled the German race", no date.

Right
"Jews out", an anti-Semitic board game published during the "Third Reich", no date.

Bottom
Title page of the "Stürmer" magazine, 14 June, 1935.

Anna Maria Strauß and her sons Adolf and Erich from Hersbruck. On 8 March, 1943, they were arrested, brought to Nuremberg and then deported to Auschwitz. All three of them were murdered there.

Persecution of Sinti and Roma

Sinti und Roma ("gypsies") were persecuted in the Third Reich for being asocial elements as well as a racially alien strain. A decree issued by the Reich Minister of the Interior of 3 January, 1936 subjected them to the Law for the Protection of German Blood and Honor. After 1936 they were confined in local internment camps. In the context of the operation against "asocials" of 1938, criminal investigation police began for the first time to transport Sinti and Roma in large numbers to concentration camps. On instructions from Himmler of 8 December, 1938 all "pure gypsies" and "gypsies with mixed blood" living in Germany were recorded, examined and classified. This provided the basis for later deportation to the extermination camps in the East.

Compulsory Sterilization and "Euthanasia"

The first victims of "racial-biological" measures were the sick and the infirm. Between 1933 and 1945 ca. 350,000 people were compulsorily sterilized on the grounds of genuine or ostensible hereditary diseases. This included many who were judged to have a hereditary defect on the basis of deviant social behavior. 5,000 people died during the operation. At the start of the war Hitler initiated "euthanasia" under the code name "Action T4": the murder of severely mentally or physically handicapped patients in nursing and mental homes. By the end of the war at least 200,000 people had fallen victim to "euthanasia".

BERLIN, 1. Sept. 1939.

Reichsleiter Bouhler und
Dr. med. Brandt

sind unter Verantwortung beauftragt, die Befug-
nisse namentlich zu bestimmender Ärzte so zu er-
weitern, dass nach menschlichem Ermessen unheilbar
Kranken bei kritischster Beurteilung ihres Krank-
heitszustandes der Gnadentod gewährt werden kann.

The permission to kill sick and disabled people given by Hitler in October 1939, was backdated to 1 September. Thus the murderous actions which were already being carried out, seemed to be necessitated by the war. The code name "Action T 4" derives from the Berlin address of the central headquarters for this operation in Tiergartenstraße 4.

The November Pogrom of 1938

The reason for the pogrom during the night of 9 to 10 November, 1938 was the assassination by a young Jew of the German diplomat Ernst vom Rath in Paris. Hitler and Goebbels were the instigators as they agreed to escalate, by means of the Party and the SA, the spontaneous riots which had broken out the day before into acts of "Popular Anger". All over Germany synagogues were set on fire, Jewish businesses destroyed and plundered. About one hundred Jews were killed; ca. 30,000 wealthy Jewish men were temporarily rounded up and imprisoned in concentration camps. The Jews had to pay for the damage at their own expense and were collectively fined one billion Reich marks as "Penance" payable to the Reich.

"Aryanization" – Legitimized Theft

Like all the "Jewish policies" the "removal of all Jews from the German economy" escalated continuously. Of the approximately 100,000 "Jewish" firms, more than half had been "aryanized" by April 1938. The rest were compulsorily closed down at the end of the year or "forcibly aryanized". With the start of deportations in the fall of 1941 all Jewish assets were confiscated and became the property of the Reich – the remaining property of the deportees as well as the frozen assets of the emigrants.

Top
The burnt-out synagogue in Essenwein-straße after the pogrom, Nuremberg, 1938.

Bottom
Advertisement for a "purely Aryan" Nuremberg business, 1938/39.

Preparation for War – NS Foreign Policy 1933 to 1939

National Socialist foreign policy was bent on war from the very outset. After the Wehrmacht (armed forces) marched into Austria and the Sudeten German territories of Czechoslovakia were taken over, the latter with the approval of England, France, and Italy, an old dream of German nationalism appeared in 1938 to be on the way to fulfillment: a common Reich for all Germans. The invasion of Czechoslovakia on 15 March, 1939 meant the change to an open policy of expansion.

"Blitzkriege" 1939–1941

When powerful German units marched into Poland without a declaration of war on 1 September, 1939, the Polish troops had little to offer in terms of resistance. With rapid mobile armored formations and using fighter-bombers, the Army advanced within three weeks to the boundary line that Hitler and Stalin had drawn just shortly before in a mutual Non-Aggression Pact. Great Britain and France, who had guaranteed the continued existence of Poland, reacted swiftly and declared war on Germany. After a phase of relative quiet the Germans occupied Denmark, Norway, Luxembourg, the Netherlands, Belgium and France in a series of rapid campaigns. In only three months they ruled over almost all of Western Europe.

Only Great Britain continued the war against the German Reich. Because it was not accessible for German ground forces owing to its insular position, it was attacked in the beginning from the air, then for the most part in the Atlantic as well as in the Mediterranean region by the submarine fleet. This was meant to disrupt the British reinforcement and supply routes. In southeastern Europe and North Africa Hitler hastened to the aid of his ally Italy. In 1941 the Wehrmacht occupied Yugoslavia and Greece. As a result of these military triumphs Hitler's popularity with the Germans rose to unparalleled levels.

Left
The troops so effectively presented during the Party Rallies served only one purpose: to march against the enemy as soon as possible. Photograph from the exhibition.

Right
German soldiers marching into Poland, 1 September, 1939.

The War of Annihilation and Genocide

22 June, 1941: The invasion of the Soviet Union was unleashed under the code name "Operation Barbarossa". This was the beginning of the war, Hitler's main concern. Several goals were to be achieved simultaneously: permanent ownership of "living space" in the East, the extermination of Bolshevism, the "solution to the Jewish question", the exploitation of raw materials and labor.

Hitler waged the war against the Soviet Union from the very beginning as a war of conquest and annihilation. The war in the Balkans, which the "Wehrmacht" had occupied, was of comparable harshness. The main agents of the war of annihilation were the SS and police complex directed by Heinrich Himmler in his capacity as Reichsführer-SS and chief of the German police. This complex encompassed the Security Police, i.e. the Secret State Police (Gestapo) and criminal police as well as the Security Service of the Reichsführer-SS (also called the SD) as well as the Order Police and the armed Waffen-SS units. The terror regime of the SS and police units is to some extent encouraged, at the least tolerated, by the Army leadership and the generals of the Eastern armies. Individual army units are also directly involved in the mass crimes.

Top
Women and children shot after the "liquidation" of the ghetto of Mizoch, Western Ukraine, on 14 October, 1942.

Bottom
Members of the Wehrmacht and the German Labour Service watching a Einsatz-gruppen sergeant shooting a Ukrainian Jew, Vinnitsa (Soviet Union), 1942.

The Task Forces

As already witnessed in Poland, but with an extended and more rigorous assignment, "task forces of the security police and the security service (SD)" advanced behind the German front. The mission of the four task forces and their extermination squads and special detachments was to "safeguard" the police and secret service activities in the occupied territories. This comprised the murder of Soviet political and administrative commissars as well as other persons considered to be "enemies of the Reich"; as of August 1941 these included all Jews and often Sinti and Roma. The task forces were mobile units of the Reich Central Security Office in Berlin and consisted of Gestapo, criminal investigation police, and the security service. They were split into subunits of a total of 3,000 men each. At least 500,000 people fell victim to the task forces.

The Role of the Wehrmacht

Under the terms of a "Commissar Decree" from the High Command of the Armed Forces, Red Army political officers, the so-called commissars, were to be shot immediately after being taken prisoner. Many – but not all – units carried out this order, which violated international law. It was just as much a violation of international law to single out "unwanted" prisoners – again commissars, party and administrative officials, Jews. They were murdered by the task forces or the Gestapo outside the camps. From the fall of 1941 prisoners who couldn't work owing to injury, illness, or frailty were starved to death. Three million Soviet soldiers died in the camps over the entire period of the war. Units from the armed forces carried out large-scale joint operations with the SS and the police against partisans, in which more often than not a greater number of innocent civilians than genuine partisans were killed. Frequently entire stretches of the country were devastated, the inhabitants murdered, expelled, or deported to forced labor camps. Individual units such as the 707th infantry division in White Russia and the 433rd infantry regiment in Serbia were specifically employed for the mass execution of Jews and "gypsies".

Holocaust

While with virtually no exception the Jewish population in the occupied Soviet territories was being executed by firing squad, in Berlin plans for the systematic murder of all European Jews were being hatched in the fall of 1941. The deportation of the Jews from the Reich began in October of this year. The series of pictures on the right show the deportation of Franconian Jews from the March Field train station near the Nazi Party Rally Grounds in November of 1941.

To handle the killing of the large number of Polish Jews, the SS set up three single-purpose extermination camps near the former Soviet border: Belzec, Sobibor and Treblinka. Polish Jews were also murdered in the extermination camps Chelmno, Lublin-Majdanek and Auschwitz-Birkenau.

Between July and October of 1942 more than 800,000 Jews were murdered in Treblinka alone. The extermination camp Auschwitz-Birkenau, also called "Auschwitz II", became the central location for the "Final Solution to the Jewish Question in Europe". By the fall of 1944 Jews from all over Europe were sent to their deaths – altogether some one million people. In February and March of 1943 23,000 Sinti and Roma were deported primarily from the German Reich to Auschwitz and isolated there in so-called gypsy camps. Most of them died of hunger and disease; the last 3,000 survivors were sent to the gas chambers in August 1944.

Altogether at least six million Jews seized by the Germans lost their lives – beaten to death, murdered, through forced labor, as a result of undernourishment and illness. A little more than half died in the extermination camps. The total number of murdered Sinti and Roma has not yet been completely clarified, but estimates fluctuate between 100,000 and 500,000.

The Result of the War

In similar manner to how the states of western and northern Europe as well as the Balkans were defeated, the Soviet Union was also to be overrun in a "lightning campaign". After huge initial successes, the German troops advanced to Leningrad and Moscow, but were not able to capture these cities. It was already at this juncture, not at the catastrophe of Stalingrad in the winter of 1942/43, that it became obvious that German forces were not sufficient to complete Hitler's program of conquest. The Red Army finally gained the upper hand in equally embittered battles with massive numbers of casualties and reached the border of the Reich in 1944.

In the same period of time British and American troops, battle by battle, drove the Wehrmacht out of North Africa, Sicily, southern and central Italy. The Allied invasion in northern France in June 1944 opened a third front against the German Reich, whose situation became more and more hopeless.

Despite all Adolf Hitler continued the battle. Up until now "only" subject to air raids, Germany in the final phases of the war became the scene of ground fighting involving heavy losses. Only after the Red Army had already occupied the government district does Hitler gave up and commited suicide in the bunker in the Reich Chancellery. The German Wehrmacht finally capitulated in the night of May 8 to 9, 1945.

In the end the Germans experienced the same violence and terror to which Germany had subjected all of Europe. Millions fled to the west or were driven out. The number of people who died while fleeing or being forcibly expelled from their homes lies between 600,000 and 2,000,000. All told the total loss of human life in this war is estimated at more than 50 million.

Top left to right

Franconian Jews being herded through the streets of Würzburg towards the railway station to be deported to an extermination camp, November 1941.

Jews from Nuremberg were gathered on the March Field before being deported to Riga, where most of them were shot, November 1941.

Finally the war ended up where it had originated from: final battle in Berlin, 1945; photograph from the exhibition.

Bottom left

Entrance Gate of the extermination camp Auschwitz-Birkenau, 1945.

The German Resistance

The German Resistance was represented by the total political spectrum. It ran the gamut from far left to far right, included the young and the old, women and men, Christians and atheists. Yet it is only a tiny minority. According to estimates by the Gestapo only two out of a thousand people were opponents of the German regime. The dictator is firmly supported by the masses. Only a handful find the inner strength to go against the tide and risk their lives.

In retrospect the Resistance can be divided into three phases: Immediately after 1933 Resistance activities are carried out primarily by the underground and exile organizations of the workers' movement. However, the political left – like the conservative bourgeois parties – had at first underestimated Hitler and was unprepared for resistance against the NS dictatorship. Only the Communists, having been ruthlessly hunted down by the police, saw themselves forced to immediately organize illegal associations.

A second phase with comparably little activity followed with opposition in the middle class camp beginning to form.

After the invasion of the Soviet Union the Resistance gained strength once again. This third phase ended on 20 July, 1944 with the failed assassination attempt on Adolf Hitler with its hoped-for overthrow of the government.

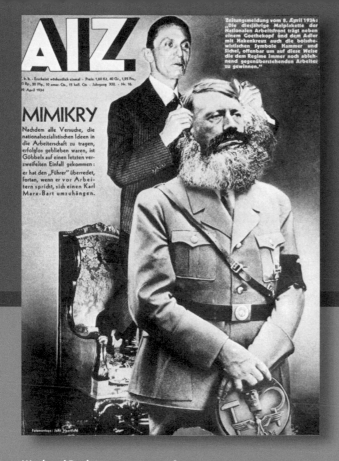

AIZ

MIMIKRY

Nachdem alle Versuche, die
nationalsozialistischen Ideen in
die Arbeiterschaft zu tragen,
erfolglos geblieben waren, ist
Göbbels auf einen letzten ver-
zweifelten Einfall gekommen:
er hat den „Führer" überredet,
fortan, wenn er vor Arbei-
tern spricht, sich einen Karl
Marx-Bart umzuhängen.

Helmut Hirsch
planned a bomb
attack during the
1937 Party Rally.
The 21-year-old
Jewish student
of architecture
was executed.

Georg Elser was
arrested shortly
after his assassi-
nation attempt
and then deported
to Dachau. He
was murdered
there in 1945.

Workers' Resistance, 1933–1936

The main agents of the resistance in the early phase were the
replacement organizations of the Communist Party, illegal
circles of former SPD members and trade unionists as well as
a few other small Socialist groupings, such as the Socialist
Workers' Party (SAP), the group Begin Anew (NB), and the International Socialist Fighters League (ISK). The Gestapo infiltrated
the illegal groups and almost without exception crushed
them all by 1936.

The Interim Phase, 1936–1941

During this period an opposition began to grow amongst the military
as well as civilians, who owing to their insider knowledge saw through
Hitler's disastrous war-mongering policies. Groups took shape which
were later to form the opposition and the resistance: the Goerdeler
Circle, the Schulze-Boysen/Harnack-Organization ("Red Orchestra"), the
Kreisau Circle, and the military opposition. The climax of this phase was
an individual act: the failed assassination attempt on Hitler by Georg
Elser on 8 November, 1939 in the Munich Bürgerbräukeller beer hall.

Photo montage by John Heartfield
on the title page of the Communist
"Workers' Illustrated Paper",
April 1934.

100

Resistance During the War, 1941–1945

The Hitler-Stalin Pact had totally stifled the Socialists and Communists. The German invasion of the Soviet Union was the signal for them to reorganize. Among others, the Uhrig-Römer and the Saefkow-Jacob organizations were formed. Again, these cadres were exposed and smashed, just as was the "Red Orchestra" and the students' resistance group the "White Rose". Hundreds were executed. The military putsch of 20 July, 1944, despite its failure, was the only resistance attempt with a realistic chance of successfully eliminating the regime, and thus ending a now senseless war. The National Socialists used the July Plot to inflict bloody revenge on the opposition.

Sophie Scholl, member of the "White Rose" resistance movement, was executed in February 1943.

Kommilitoninnen! Kommilitonen!

Erschüttert steht unser Volk vor dem Untergang der Männer von Stalingrad. Dreihundertdreissigtausend deutsche Männer hat die geniale Strategie des Weltkriegsgefreiten sinn- und verantwortungslos in Tod und Verderben gehetzt. Führer, wir danken dir!

Es gärt im deutschen Volk: Wollen wir weiter einem Dilettanten das Schicksal unserer Armeen anvertrauen? Wollen wir den niedrigen Machtinstinkten einer Parteiclique den Rest der deutschen Jugend opfern? Nimmermehr!

Der Tag der Abrechnung ist gekommen, der Abrechnung unserer deutschen Jugend mit der verabscheuungswürdigsten Tyrannis, die unser Volk je erduldet hat. Im Namen der ganzen deutschen Jugend fordern wir von dem Staat Adolf Hitlers die persönliche Freiheit, das kostbarste Gut des Deutschen zurück, um das er uns in der erbärmlichsten Weise betrogen hat.

In einem Staat rücksichtsloser Knebelung jeder freien Meinungsäusserung sind wir aufgewachsen. HJ, SA, SS haben uns in den fruchtbarsten Bildungsjahren unseres Lebens zu uniformieren, zu revolutionieren, zu narkotisieren versucht. „Weltanschauliche Schulung" hiess die verächtliche Methode, das aufkeimende Selbstdenken und Selbstwerten in einem Nebel leerer Phrasen zu ersticken. Eine Führerauslese, wie sie teuflischer und bornierter zugleich nicht gedacht werden kann, sieht ihre künftigen Parteibonzen auf Ordensburgen zu gottlosen, schamlosen und gewissenlosen Ausbeutern und Mordbuben heran, zur blinden, stupiden Führergefolgschaft. Wir „Arbeiter des Geistes" wären gerade recht, dieser neuen Herrenschicht den Knüppel zu machen. Frontkämpfer werden von Studentenführern und Gauleiteraspiranten wie Schuljungen gemassregelt, Gauleiter greifen mit geilen Spässen den Studentinnen an die Ehre. Deutsche Studentinnen haben an der Münchner Hochschule auf die Besudelung ihrer Ehre eine würdige Antwort gegeben, deutsche Studenten haben sich für ihre Kameradinnen eingesetzt und standgehalten. Das ist ein Anfang zur Erkämpfung unserer freien Selbstbestimmung, ohne die geistige Werte nicht geschaffen werden können. Unser Dank gilt den tapferen Kameradinnen und Kameraden, die mit leuchtendem Beispiel vorangegangen sind!

Es gibt für uns nur eine Parole: Kampf gegen die Partei! Heraus aus den Parteigliederungen, in denen man uns politisch weiter mundtot halten will! Heraus aus den Hörsälen der SS- Unter- oder Oberführer und Parteikriecher! Es geht uns um wahre Wissenschaft und echte Geistesfreiheit! Kein Drohmittel kann uns schrecken, auch nicht die Schliessung unserer Hochschulen. Es gilt den Kampf jedes einzelnen von uns um unsere Zukunft, unsere Freiheit und Ehre in einem seiner sittlichen Verantwortung bewussten Staatswesen.

Freiheit und Ehre! Zehn lange Jahre haben Hitler und seine Genossen die beiden herrlichen deutschen Worte bis zum Ekel ausgequetscht, abgedroschen, verdreht, wie es nur Dilettanten vermögen, die die höchsten Werte einer Nation vor die Säue werfen. Was ihnen Freiheit und Ehre gilt, haben sie in zehn Jahren der Zerstörung aller materiellen und geistigen Freiheit, aller sittlichen Substanz im deutschen Volk genugsam gezeigt. Auch dem dümmsten Deutschen hat das furchtbare Blutbad die Augen geöffnet, das sie im Namen von Freiheit und Ehre der deutschen Nation in ganz Europa angerichtet haben und täglich neu anrichten. Der deutsche Name bleibt für immer geschändet, wenn nicht die deutsche Jugend endlich aufsteht, rächt und sühnt zugleich, seine Peiniger zerschmettert und ein neues, geistiges Europa aufrichtet.

Studentinnen! Studenten! Auf uns sieht das sieht das deutsche Volk! Von uns erwartet es, wie 1813 die Brechung des Napoleonischen, so 1943 die Brechung des nationalsozialistischen Terrors aus der Macht des Geistes. Beresina und Stalingrad flammen im Osten auf, die Toten von Stalingrad beschwören uns!

„Frisch auf, mein Volk, die Flammenzeichen rauchen!"

Unser Volk steht im Aufbruch gegen die Verknechtung Europas durch den Nationalsozialismus, im neuen gläubigen Durchbruch von Freiheit und Ehre!

The Nuremberg Trials

After the end of the war, the trial of main National Socialist war criminals was held by the International Military Tribunal (IMT) in Nuremberg. After this trial, American military tribunals in Nuremberg also held twelve "follow-up trials" against leading personalities from the "Third Reich". Already during the war, the USA, the Soviet Union and Great Britain had decided on the criminal prosecution of the main National Socialist criminals. In August 1945, France was also included in the treaty on the "Prosecution and Punishment of the Main War Criminals".

The former "City of the Party Rallies" was chosen as the venue for this trial for symbolic, but mainly also for practical reasons. The American government insisted on a venue within its occupied zone, and in Nuremberg, an undamaged court building, as well as a suitable prison were available. The trials of the main war criminals started on 20 November, 1945. The indictment contained four counts: crimes against peace, war crimes, crimes against humanity and a common plan and conspiracy to commit those crimes.

The International Military Tribunal

After the German capitulation on 8/9 May, 1945 the victors – the USA, the USSR, Great Britain, and France – set up an International Military Tribunal with headquarters in Berlin on 8 August, 1945. It convened in Criminal Courtroom 600 in Nuremberg's Court of Justice.

The Nuremberg court was located in the American zone of occupation, explaining why the US military government was responsible for organizing the trial. It took care of the accommodation and feeding of those involved in the trials; it guarded the defendants and cordoned off the Justice building. Moreover, it had to obtain and evaluate the NS files as well as hire specialists. Each of the four victorious powers was represented in the trial with its own judges and prosecutors.

The Course of the Trial

Sitting in the dock at the "Nuremberg Trial", which lasted from 20 November, 1945 to 1 October, 1946, were 21 representatives of the NS regime. (Martin Bormann was tried in absentia; the charges against Gustav Krupp von Bohlen and Halbach were dropped, because he was physically unable to stand trial. Robert Ley, who had also been indicted, committed suicide before the trial started.) The Reich cabinet, the NSDAP leadership corps, the Gestapo, the Security Service, SS and SA as well as the General Staff and the High Command of the Wehrmacht were all indicted as criminal organizations. The trial was based on thousands of pieces of written evidence and hundreds of testimonies by witnesses.

The defendants, 1945/46.

Bottom row, from the left: Hermann Göring, Rudolf Heß, Joachim von Ribbentrop, Wilhelm Keitel, Ernst Kaltenbrunner, Alfred Rosenberg, Hans Frank, Wilhelm Frick, Julius Streicher, Walther Funk, Hjalmar Schacht.

Top row from the left: Karl Dönitz, Erich Raeder, Baldur von Schirach, Fritz Sauckel, Alfred Jodl, Franz von Papen (standing), Arthur Seyß-Inquart, Albert Speer, Konstantin Freiherr von Neurath, Hans Fritzsche.

Left
"Millions of war dead waiting for the proclamation of the sentence and the punishment for these incredible crimes." Cartoon by David Low in the "Evening Standard" of 24 September, 1946.

Right
Title page of the special edition of the "Süddeutsche Zeitung" of 1 October, 1946.

104

The Verdict

On 30 September and 1 October, 1946 the judges announced the verdicts: Twelve of the defendants were sentenced to death, three to life imprisonment and four to long-term imprisonment. Three defendants were acquitted. The International Military Tribunal handed down verdicts of guilty to the criminal organizations of the NSDAP leadership corps, the Gestapo, the SD, and the SS (with the exception of the SS mounted regiments). On 16 October, 1946 those sentenced to death were executed in Nuremberg.

Sonderausgabe
Preis 15 Pfg.

Süddeutsche Zeitung

MÜNCHNER NACHRICHTEN AUS POLITIK · KULTUR · WIRTSCHAFT UND SPORT

München, Dienstag, 1. Oktober 1946

Die Sühne der Hauptkriegsverbrecher

Das Urteil in Nürnberg

12 Todesurteile
Schacht, Papen und Fritzsche freigesprochen

Nürnberg, 1. Oktober (SZ. Dana)

In der Dienstagnachmittag-Verhandlung um 15.55 Uhr gab der Nürnberger Oberste Militärgerichtshof das Urteil gegen die einzelnen Hauptangeklagten bekannt, das von der ganzen Welt mit ungeheurer Spannung erwartet wurde und den Schlußstein setzt unter eine Bilanz von Völkermord und Verbrechen furchtbaren Ausmaßes. Lordrichter Lawrence verkündete folgendes Strafmaß:

Zum Tode verurteilt:

Göring:	Tod durch Strang
Ribbentrop:	Tod durch Strang
Keitel:	Tod durch Strang
Kaltenbrunner:	Tod durch Strang
Rosenberg:	Tod durch Strang
Frank:	Tod durch Strang
Frick:	Tod durch Strang
Streicher:	Tod durch Strang
Sauckel:	Tod durch Strang
Jodl:	Tod durch Strang
Seyß-Inquart:	Tod durch Strang

Schacht:	nicht schuldig nach allen Anklagepunkten, sofortige Entlassung nach Ende der Verhandlung angeordnet.
Papen:	nicht schuldig nach allen Anklagepunkten, sofortige Entlassung nach Ende der Verhandlung angeordnet.
Fritzsche:	nicht schuldig nach allen Anklagepunkten, sofortige Entlassung nach Ende der Verhandlung angeordnet.

In Abwesenheit:

Bormann:	zum Tode durch den Strang verurteilt.

Lebenslänglich Gefängnis:

Heß:	lebenslängliches Gefängnis
Funk:	lebenslängliches Gefängnis
Raeder:	lebenslängliches Gefängnis

Gefängnisstrafen:

Dönitz:	zehn Jahre Gefängnis
Neurath:	fünfzehn Jahre Gefängnis
Schirach:	zwanzig Jahre Gefängnis
Speer:	zwanzig Jahre Gefängnis

Letzte Meldung:

...

"Im Namen der Gerechtigkeit"

...

Photo captions:
Göring: zum Tode
Heß: lebenslänglich
Ribbentrop: zum Tode
Keitel: zum Tode
Kaltenbrunner: zum Tode
Rosenberg: zum Tode
Frank: zum Tode
Frick: zum Tode
Funk: lebenslänglich
Streicher: zum Tode
Schacht: nicht schuldig
Sauckel: zum Tode
Jodl: zum Tode
Papen: nicht schuldig
Seyß-Inquart: zum Tode
Speer: Zwanzig Jahre
Neurath: Fünfzehn Jahre
Dönitz: zehn Jahre
Raeder: lebenslänglich
Fritzsche: nicht schuldig
Schirach: Zwanzig Jahre
Bormann: zum Tode

(Fortsetzung auf Seite 2)

The head of the SS Economics and Administrative Department, Oswald Pohl, during his testimony in the "IG Farben Trial", on 3 November, 1947. In the background, a panel showing the armament manufacturing plants of IG Farben in Auschwitz-Monowitz.

The Subsequent Proceedings

The "Nuremberg Trial" was not the only attempt to prosecute those who had committed NS crimes. Numerous other war crimes trials were held before the military courts of the occupation forces and in the territories formerly occupied by the Germans. Between 1946 and 1949 177 high-ranking doctors, lawyers, and industrialists, SS and police officers, military officers, civil servants and diplomats stood trial in twelve subsequent proceedings before US military courts. The proceedings demonstrated the extent to which the Germany establishment had contributed to the rise and functioning of the NS regime.

The Nazi Party Rally Grounds after 1945

After 1945 ownership of the Nazi Party Rally Grounds was transferred to the City of Nuremberg, which had once provided a large expanse of ground for the National Socialist construction site. As in many other German cities there was for many decades little or no awareness of the special historical significance of the NS buildings. Since 1973 the structural remains of the former Party Rally Grounds have become listed sites. As a reaction to the increasing public interest in the National Socialist past, the City of Nuremberg set up an exhibition inside the Zeppelin Tribune, which saw the Nazi Party Rally Grounds as a "Learning Centre for German History". In November 2001 the Documentation Centre Nazi Party Rally Grounds was opened in the north wing of the Congress Hall.

Top
Disposing of the remains in Luitpold Grove, in July 1949: the "Street of the Führer" between the Hall of Honour and the rostrum opposite is being demolished. The stands which can still be seen to the left and right, were also removed.

Bottom
Luitpold Grove, the Congress Hall above, with Volksfestplatz and greater and lesser Dutzendteich lakes; the Great Street; top right, Zeppelin Field to the left. Early 1960s.

Zeppelin Field

In 1945 the US Army blew up the large swastika on the main tribune of the Zeppelin Field. For the next few years it held its parades there. In 1945/46 ownership of the Zeppelin Field property was transferred back to the municipal authorities. Since then open-air events of every kind have been held on the grounds.

The Former Camp Zone

After 1945 the POW camp in Langwasser was used first as an American internment and international refugee camp. Later it became the Federal reception camp for foreigners. From the 1950s the suburb of Langwasser was built where the camp had once stood as well as on other parts of the former Party Rally Grounds.

From top to bottom

Motor cycle race in the 1950s.

Row of pillars on Zeppelin Grandstand, blown up because they were dilapidated, on 8/9 June, 1967.

Blowing up of a March Field tower, 22 April, 1967.

The Congress Hall

After 1945 ownership of the building passed over to the municipal authorities. It was used from then on for practical purposes. In September 1949 the First German Construction Exhibition took place here and on the grounds of the Great Road. In July 1950 the City of Nuremberg used the building for a jubilee exhibition as part of its 900th anniversary celebrations. Afterwards a variety of very practical uses was found for it.

Conversion Projects

Plans to demolish the Congress Hall or convert it into a sports stadium were rejected because of the costs involved. In 1987 a company intended to turn the building into a recreational and shopping centre. Objections by the Bavarian State Office for the Preservation of Historic Monuments and greater public sensitivity towards dealing with NS buildings put an end to these questionable plans.

Top
Stall of the Association of the Granite Industry on the German Building Exhibition in the Congress Hall, 1949.

Bottom
Report on the "Nürnberger Nachrichten" about the suggestion to convert the Congress Hall into a football stadium, 5 May, 1962.

Top
The unfinished shell of the
Congress Hall seen across the lesser
Dutzendteich lake, around 1955.

Bottom
Refurbished entrance hall of
the Zeppelin Grandstand with first
exhibition "Fascination and Terror".

Right
The way back: Looking the stake
down from the end of the exhibition
towards the entrance hall, 2014.

Dutzendteich Public Park

The grounds surrounding the two Dutzendteich lakes had been a traditional Nuremberg recreational area before 1933. In the 1950s the Dutzendteich public park was laid out on this area. The Luitpold Grove, which has been converted into a park, lies nearby. The tribune buildings erected there after 1933 and the "Street of the *Führer*" yielded to a large grassy lawn.

Restoration

Since 1973 the Congress Hall, built in the "Monumental Style of the Third Reich", has been designated a listed building. This obliges the City of Nuremberg to maintain the fabric of the NS relics. In 1984 the mosaic ceiling in the entrance hall of the Zeppelin brandstand was restored, a few years later the Great Road. The former SS barracks have also been accorded listed-building status.

Imprint

Publisher:
Museen der Stadt Nürnberg
Dokumentationszentrum Reichsparteitagsgelände

Editor:
Hans-Christian Täubrich

Compilation:
Dr. Martina Christmeier

Texts:
Dr. Eckart Dietzfelbinger
(Essays on the Congress Hall and the Documentation Centre)

For all other texts which were taken from the exhibition
"Fascination and Terror" were responsible:
Dr. Volker Dahm, Institut für Zeitgeschichte München,
Dr. Friedrich Kießling, Universität Erlangen-Nürnberg,
Prof. Dr. Horst Möller, Institut für Zeitgeschichte München,
Prof. Dr. Gregor Schöllgen, Universität Erlangen-Nürnberg,
Museen der Stadt Nürnberg

Publishing house:
Druckhaus Nürnberg

Layout:
Martin Küchle

© Dokumentationszentrum Reichsparteitagsgelände Nürnberg

Contact:
Museen der Stadt Nürnberg
Dokumentationszentrum Reichsparteitagsgelände
Bayernstraße 110, 90478 Nürnberg
Tel. (0911) 231-5666, Fax (0911) 231-8410
E-Mail:dokumentationszentrum@stadt.nuernberg.de
Website: www.museen.nuernberg.de

NÜRNBERG

■ Organisation Chart